THE HEAVENS DECLARE THE GLORY OF GOD *Psalm 19. 1*

Spiral Nebula in Triangulum. Messier 33. Mount Wilson. 60-in Refl.

Photo: By courtesy of the Mount Wilson and Palomar Observatories

Westwood, New Jersey
London, E.C.4—29 Ludgate Hill
Glasgow, C.2—229 Bothwell Street

First published - 1964
Reprinted -   - 1965

CREATION REVEALED

A Study of Genesis Chapter One in the
Light of Modern Science

FREDK. A. FILBY
M.Sc., Ph.D.(London), F.R.I.C.

Foreword by

R. L. F. BOYD
Ph.D., M.I.E.E.

Professor of Physics at University College in the University of London
and Professor of Astronomy in the Royal Institution

FLEMING H. REVELL COMPANY

TO THE MEMORY OF MY FATHER
WHO FIRST INTERESTED ME IN
GENESIS AND GEOLOGY

PREFACE

THIS book is the result of some thirty years' study of the Biblical account of Creation on the one hand, and of some aspects of Science on the other. It makes no claim to solve all the problems that such a study invariably encounters. It certainly does not set out to prove that there is a Creator or that the Genesis account was inspired by that Creator. Both of these are accepted as foundation truths. The aim is not argument but constructive thought. I have tried to see what light God intended us to gather from His Word—and I have suggested that we can gather more as time goes on. And I have tried to see what light God has permitted us to gather from scientific studies—and here too the amount increases year by year. The conviction grows upon me that there is a great deal in common in these two aspects of truth and I have not hesitated to say so—hence this book. It will not convince, and really is not meant to convince, those whose minds are already closed by a determined adherence to atheistical materialism, or to random evolution, or to the myth and legend theory of Genesis. Nor on the other hand will it satisfy those who, by insisting that every word of Genesis must be taken literally, deny to the Creator the right to use metaphors and figures of speech if He so will. It is written for those who can keep a sufficiently open mind to ask what the Bible really reveals and what science really proves. To me the answer is the same in both cases—the Wisdom and Glory of God.

It remains only to add my very sincere thanks to those who have helped me: to Dr. Stephen S. Short for very many valuable suggestions; to Mr. David Ellis, B.D., for help with the transliteration of Hebrew words; to Prof. R. Boyd for helpful suggestions and for writing the Foreword; and, indeed, to all of these, together with Mr. G. C. D. Howley, for real encouragement in the publication of this book. Last, and by no means least, my thanks are due to my wife who, with endless care and patience, has helped me in the correction and preparation of the manuscript for publication.

ILFORD,
November, 1962

CONTENTS

FOREWORD

THE gulf between the scientist and the non-scientist is as wide today as it ever was. By no means the least of the ills that have resulted from this lack of *rapport* is the deification, or at any rate the idolisation, of science in the minds of men. On the one hand, too many scientists, obsessed with the success that has attended the study of *mechanism* and *pattern* in the world of Nature, have, from long disuse, lost both the desire and the faculty to explore the *meaning* and the *purpose*. On the other hand, many non-scientists, understanding neither the aim nor the method of science, have mistaken technological prowess for the evidence of true understanding and skill with strange words for the right to the last word.

In the hot pursuit of the explanation and the exploitation of phenomena few find time to wonder and fewer still to worship. Yet beyond all the complexity of our mathematics, beyond the rationality of our natural laws and the challenge of the unreduced, the unexplained and even the unknown, stands the stark fact of existence, the mystery of being, more challenging than all the gaps in our knowledge, more wonderful than all the explanations and formulae—a perpetual and insistent call to humility and worship.

What character of worship shall the mystery of self and of the cosmos evoke? How shall we conceive of the Eternal? As Isaiah said, long ago, 'To whom then will ye liken God or what likeness will ye compare unto Him?' It is unthinkable that the Ultimate, the Giver of the whole from Whom all things proceed, should be likened to a mere part or component of the Universe. Shall then the creature bow before creation itself and Nature receive the worship her mystery should evoke?

To the philosophic mind, unaided by any revelation, some such pantheism would seem to be the only alternative to agnosticism. Such is the dilemma of natural religion unless indeed faith is to be reduced to an earthbound and parochial humanism. But the mind of Man has no need to grope unaided. To the Jew and to the Christian, God is a God Who speaks. He is to be sought, yes and found too, not as a Super-phenomenon to be observed but as a Personality to be encountered. He is the 'I am' Who spoke to Moses, Who revealed Himself when 'The Word was made flesh' and Who still speaks by His Spirit in the hearts of men. 'When in former times' says the writer to the Hebrews, 'God spoke to our forefathers, He spoke in fragmentary and varied fashion through the prophets. But in this final age He has spoken to us in the Son.'

Amongst these partial and varied revelations of God is the sublime first chapter of Genesis, incomparably more restrained than the creation myths of the heathen, truer because more absolute than any mere statement of scientific fact. Because it establishes our creatureliness it is more relevant than all the ethics and morals of unrevealed religion. This chapter outlives and will continue to outlive the naïvety of those who bind God to an unpoetic literalism and lose the message of the wood amongst the trees of dogma or of doubt.

This book is not for those who, learning their science from Nature, are unwilling to learn aught else from any other source; neither is it for those who, unwilling to submit their minds to the discipline of science, deprive God of the worship of that part of their being and impiously seek by a futile short cut to learn their science from the Bible.

Dr. Filby has practised and taught Chemistry for many years. Deeply involved also, throughout these years, in the worship and service of the Church, he has meditated as scientist and as Christian on this opening chapter of the Bible. This book is the result of his meditation.

In commending it to the Christian reader I would say: Look not for the answer to your curiosity nor only for that which science has discovered or may yet hope to discover, but look beyond the mere mechanism of God's activity to its meaning and get a fresh glimpse of the greatness of your God, for here is a book that should bow you in worship. Remember, as you read, that it is said of Him Who walked the streets of Nazareth and climbed the hill of Calvary that through Him God 'created all orders of existence. The Son Who is the effulgence of God's splendour and the stamp of God's very being . . . sustains the universe by His word of power.'

R. L. F. BOYD, Ph.D., M.I.E.E.

Professor of Physics at University College in the University of London and Professor of Astronomy in the Royal Institution

CHAPTER 1

THE PURPOSE AND STYLE OF GENESIS 1

THE Bible is a complete book. It is a book that is plainly intended to be complete in itself. It has, and is plainly intended to have, its limits, for out of all the vast number of objects that exist in this universe it is concerned with but one, namely this tiny earth, and out of all the types of living creatures on this planet it deals with but one, namely man. Yet further, out of all the countless ages that must have run their course it is concerned only with the few thousands of years which centre around the coming of Jesus Christ to this earth. It is the story of one race, on one planet, in one age. Such a story, if it is to be complete, must have a beginning and it must have an end, an Alpha and an Omega. Here and there the book may peer back beyond the beginning of our planet into a remote past. Elsewhere its light may shine into a future when this Earth shall be so changed as to justify the expression 'A new heaven and a new earth', and the Omega of this age may merge into the Alpha of the next, but apart from these wonderful glimpses the Bible is the story of one race, on one planet, in one age. With that, and with a promise of the Way into the Age beyond, we must be content. Whether any other races have ever existed in other ages on other planets, or will exist, it is not the intention of the Book to tell us. From some indirect and sometimes uncertain interpretations of isolated passages, and from certain philosophical considerations we may surmise a little, but the Book as a whole is intended to be a story of only one race, on one planet, in one age. That story must have a beginning and that beginning is Genesis 1. Without it the Bible would be imperfect: with it the Book is complete.

There is a second reason for the existence of Genesis 1. As we grow up we become conscious of our surroundings; of an environment which includes light and darkness, land and sea and sky, sun and moon and stars, birds, beasts and fishes; a vast and wonderful environment which in science we explore, but which

13

nevertheless sets us a problem. We ask, 'Where did it all come from, who controls it, what is my place in it?'

Men have given various answers. Some say that they do not know and are sure that no one else knows, or will ever know. Some assert that the universe just 'happened' and that we just 'happened' also: we are the chance product of our environment: we are just made of matter and energy—earth, air, fire and water —and no more.

No more! But there is a deep conviction within most of us that there *is* something more. The amazing pattern which science reveals around us, even though we may not yet fit all the parts together, and the irrepressible voice of conscience within, even though its voice be sometimes dimmed by too self-centred an outlook in life, compel us to seek for a more satisfying answer. That answer is, once again, Genesis 1.

From the very commencement the Book declares that man is not the chance product of the universe. Genesis 1 was written to establish that the God revealed in the rest of the Book by the Law and the Prophets and supremely by His Son, that that God, and He alone, created both man and the universe.

The reasons then for the existence of Genesis 1 are at least twofold. It forms the beginning of a complete story. It establishes that the God revealed in the Bible and in the Person of Christ, is the one and only Creator of all things visible and invisible.

For whom then was this chapter written? The first chapter of a book is usually intended for the readers of the book. But who are the readers of this Book? Although the book was written in the midst of the habitable earth, it has spread to east and west, to north and south, and from the Old World to the New. Its readers can be found in each of the continents; they can be found within the Arctic Circle as well as on the Equator. Its readers can be found in cottages, in palaces, in factories, in universities, in ships and in tents. Its readers seem in fact to be the human race . . . or at least representative of every part of that race. Nor is this surprising. If it is the story of one race, on one planet, in one age, surely it is intended for the members of that one race.

But if this is so, it at once imposes the most drastic limitations upon the style that can be employed in the chapter. The style must suit all classes of people in all ages.

It has been said that the account of Creation might be given in one of three ways:—(a) scientific, (b) straightforward historical prose, (c) poetry. The problem is not, however, so easy of solution.

Let us consider first the possibility of a scientific account of the creation of the universe and of this planet and its inhabitants. The account to be truly scientific must be accurate against a background of ultimate reality. In what language could it be written? The sciences which probe most deeply into the ultimate facts of matter and life are probably astro- and nuclear physics and biochemistry . . . but these sciences are written, not so much in language as in symbols. It takes many pages of symbols to discuss the nature of a single atom of hydrogen. It has been estimated that to give a complete account of the position of the groups and bonds in a single virus of 'molecular weight 300 million' would take a 200 page book.

If the scientific description of a single hydrogen atom, or of a virus too small to be seen without a microscope, takes a book, what hope is there of ever giving a scientific account of the creation of man and the universe? Yet Genesis 1 in its original form uses only 76 different root words. If Genesis 1 were written in absolute scientific language to give an account of creation there is no man alive, nor ever has there been, who could understand it. If it were written in any kind of scientific language only the favoured few could comprehend it. It would have to be rewritten every generation to conform to the new views and terms of science. It could not be written in our mid-twentieth century scientific language, for no earlier generation could have grasped its meaning, and to our children it would be out-of-date. The scientific description of the 'How' of the universe is beyond the understanding of any human brain, but Genesis 1 was written for *all* readers, not for *none*.

A straightforward historical account of the facts, with no attempt to explain the 'how' of creation would obviously seem the best. The Creator need only state that He *did* make sun, moon, stars, land and sea . . . and this of course is what Genesis does, or nearly so. For while it is easy to speak of the Creator 'doing' things, making, seeing, commanding, fashioning . . . these very words have limited human meanings. In fact our language has no adequate words for the true historical description of what God did. The historical method is itself limited by the limitations of human language. Man is compelled to use figures of speech and to describe the actions of the Almighty Creator in words which he uses for himself. God, in Genesis 1, is compelled to take our limited human words and use them, but always with a vaster and deeper meaning than is conveyed by their ordinary significance.

The third possible method of attaining the required object was to compose Genesis 1 as a poem. Poetry, especially Eastern, relies upon the twin forms of rhythmic order or pattern of words or ideas, and highly coloured figures of speech. In Psalm 104 we have a poetical account of Creation. There are not only rhythmic patterns but beautiful figures of speech; the Creator lays the beams of His chambers in the waters, He makes the winds His messengers, the clouds His chariot: the mountains smoke at His touch and the earth trembles at His look. But here the very boldness of the metaphors and figures makes it difficult to interpret the words in anything approaching a straightforward historical manner.

Yet it is quite certain that the careful consideration either of nature or of beauty often compels man to express himself in poetry. A great scientist once said that the poets get nearer to reality than do the scientists.

What then would be the best method for the Creator to use for (1) making a beginning to His book and (2) establishing that the God of the Bible is also the God of creation—in language simple enough for all men in all time?

The answer is . . . Genesis 1 . . . the most amazing composition in all the world's literature, using only 76 different word-forms fundamental to all mankind, arranged in a wonderful poetical pattern yet free from any highly coloured figures of speech. It provides the perfect opening to God's book and establishes all that men really need to know of the *facts* of creation. No man could have invented it: it is as great a marvel as a plant or a bird. It is God's handiwork, sufficient for Hebrew children or Greek thinkers or Latin Christians; for mediaeval knights or modern scientists or little children; for cottage dwellers or cattle ranchers or deep sea fishermen; for Laplanders or Ethiopians, East or West, rich or poor, old or young, simple or learned . . . sufficient for all! Only God could write such a chapter . . . and He did.

CHAPTER 2

THE STRUCTURE OF GENESIS 1

THE structure of Genesis 1 is set out on page 16a. Its amazing simplicity of style is at once apparent. It is based on a scheme of three numbers, three, seven and ten. Yet when we come to a close inspection it will be seen that this structure is not so forced as to make each section equal or the repetitions run with absolute mathematical precision. The designing mind behind Genesis 1 is obviously that of a mathematician, but the facts of the account are not distorted in any way to make them fit the scheme. Apart from the sevens the rest of the pattern might truly be said to be 'unconscious'.

Let us now consider this pattern. There are seven days; six of them have evening and morning, the seventh has neither. The six are plainly divided into two sets of three whose story we shall follow in detail later; briefly they are:

1. Light
2. Sky and ocean
3. Land and plants

4. Light. Sun, moon and stars
5. Sky and ocean. Birds and fishes
6. Land. Animals and man
7. Rest

Seven times we are told that God 'saw'.

1. Light
2. Land and sea
3. Plant life

4. Sun and moon
5. Marine life and birds
6. Animal life
7. 'Everything that He had made'

Seven times the answer comes back—'that it was good'. Yet even here the seven are divided into six and one, for six times 'it was good' but on the seventh it was 'very good'. As we glance back at the summary of the six times that God saw 'that it was good' we shall notice the same division into two sets of three, but this is not attained by slavishly following the pattern of the days but by a new arrangement which still brings the final total to seven.

Seven times God commands the forces of His universe by the

17

words 'Let there be . . .', but once again the seven are not forced either to one per day for seven days or to the same pattern as the seven times that God 'saw that it was good'. The seven commands, three of which are double making ten in all, are:

1. Day 1 Let there be light.
2.   „   2 Let there be a firmament, and let it divide . . .
3.   „   3 Let the waters be gathered,
                          and let the dry land appear . . .
4.   „   3 Let the earth put forth grass.
5.   „   4 Let there be lights . . .
                          and let them be for signs . . .
6.   „   5 Let the waters bring forth moving creatures.
7.   „   6 Let the earth bring forth living creatures.

Once again there is a clear indication of a form of parallelism.

Nos. 1, 2 and 5 deal with sky and light.
      3 and 6   „   „   water and life in it.
      4 and 7   „   „   earth and life on it.

Finally, after these ten commands to His universe, God turns, as it were to Himself, and states the great conclusion of the divine plan:

Let us make man in our own image
Let them have dominion.

If we ask why these last should be so signally different from the preceding commands, surely the simple answer comes back that of all things thus created only man would ever read the account, and that the Creator condescends to explain that he was in a special way the product of Divine contemplation as well as creation. God, we may say, took special thought within Himself before He made beings who could think within themselves.

So then we have, in all, twelve statements commencing with the authoritative word 'let'.

Three, seven, ten, twelve—the outstanding numbers of Hebrew symbolism!

Three times we read that 'God created'. He created the heaven and the earth (v. 1), He created the marine creatures (v. 21) and He created man (v. 27). Three times we read that 'God made'. He made the firmament (v. 7), He made the two great lights[1] (v. 16)

---

[1] It does not repeat the verb for the stars. The original has just 'The stars also'.

and He made the beasts (v. 25). Three times God Himself names things: Day and night (v. 5), Heaven (v. 8), Earth and seas (v. 10). Three times God separates or divides: Light from darkness (v. 4), Clouds from oceans (v. 7), Day from night (v. 18). Three times God gives His blessing: The marine creatures (v. 22), Man (v. 28), The Sabbath (ch. 2 v. 3).

Ten times God speaks. Ten times[1] we read, 'And God said'. Precursor it may be of the Ten words He spoke in the Decalogue centuries later . . . but be that as it may, the number ten is unmistakably there.

Thus the numbers so full of symbolism to an Eastern people, three, seven, ten and twelve, are woven into the structure of the Creation story, yet not so obtrusively that the sequence of thought has to be disturbed to fit the scheme, but so perfectly that as the account reaches its conclusion so its numerical scheme attains completion.

If it be asked why this should be we may observe that the profoundest human thought is often recorded in mathematical forms. The pattern is discernible in music, in architecture, in poetry. But further, the mathematical pattern is in nature—God's handiwork—itself. The structures of molecules, the lattices of crystals, the arrangements of leaves on a stem, the details of the tiny cells of living things and their processes of division, all follow a mathematical scheme. Thoughtful minds have discerned something of the mathematical pattern of the Universe, and some of these were scientists but some were poets, and sometimes the poets have got nearer to reality than have the scientists.

It is but one step further to realise that the Mathematical Mind that designed the universe has revealed Itself through the pattern of the words of Genesis 1.

Two more observations remain to be made before we leave the consideration of the structure of Genesis 1. The Hebrew writers frequently enclosed their poems or paragraphs in a kind of 'envelope', an opening phrase and a concluding phrase to balance it. So it is here. In vv. 1-2, In the beginning God created, and His Spirit moved; in ch. 2 vv. 1-2 at the end God finished and God rested.

---

[1] Verses 3, 6, 9, 11, 14, 20, 24, 26, 28, 29. The word *min* (=kind) occurs 10 times in Genesis 1.

The last, and perhaps the strangest, observation concerns the little word *and*, the Hebrew *waw*. In its Hebrew form it is just one letter, a tiny hook, but it is this little hook that links the Bible together. In the Revised Version it will be seen that after verse 1 which commences, 'In the beginning', every verse of chapter 1, and the first three verses of chapter 2 which so obviously belong to the section, *all* begin with *and*. There is no doubt that it has many shades of meaning only to be determined by the context, and often it would be better rendered by 'so' or 'now' or 'but', yet the fact remains that in Hebrew it is always the same little hook, *waw*, which joins every verse of the section to its predecessor. Verse 4 of chapter 2 is a tablet summary, and the next section of the Bible commences at verse 5 which is provided with the opening *waw* to join it to the previous section. And so indeed every section not only of Genesis but of the Pentateuch is linked by *and* to its predecessor. Even beyond this it is true that every fresh historical section of the Old Testament begins with *waw*.

We come back then to a statement that we made at the beginning. The Bible is a complete account. It not only had to have a beginning, Genesis 1, but all the rest is actually linked on to that beginning; one might almost say, hooked on by the little word *vaw*.

CHAPTER 3

THE BACKGROUND OF GENESIS 1

WE must pause now to consider two viewpoints which have done much to obscure the true meaning and value of Genesis 1. The first of these loses sight of the chapter altogether in the study of its alleged background. The second assumes the background to be so primitive as to render the chapter useless.

This chapter—so runs the idea in the minds of some—is a late compilation by unknown Jewish writers who studied, simplified and gradually refined the older cosmologies of Assyria and Babylonia. These writers (so we are told, and imaginary diagrams are sometimes added to give strength to the assertion) pictured a flat earth which was hollow underneath (where Sheol lay) except for some massive pillars upbearing it. This earth was surmounted by an arched, solid, celestial dome, to which belonged sun, moon and stars, resting either upon the great sea which surrounded the earth or upon some yet more distant mountains which surrounded the primeval ocean. The fact that Genesis 1 differs completely from this picture is easily accounted for by these theorists with the naïve explanation that the Jewish writers had so greatly altered the Assyrian or Babylonian original as to make the two accounts different!

Genesis 1, we are told, was written in the fifth century B.C. by an anonymous writer of the priestly order with the somewhat base motive of bolstering up the divinely-given command to keep the Sabbath. Some writers, of course, go further and deny that there ever was any divine command to bolster up, but we cannot pause to examine every pale reflection of the original lie of him who said, 'Yea, hath God said?'

It was confidently asserted, some fifty years ago, that Genesis 1 was a refined edition of the Assyrian and Babylonian Legends of Creation. The first tablets giving an account of these legends were those found among the ruins of the library of King Ashurbanipal in Nineveh between 1848 and 1876 and as their contents were not fully understood for many years there may possibly have been some excuse for early translators imagining a resemblance between some phrases and the Creation account in the Bible. Since those days many additional tablets have been found, some in quite recent times, and there are now parts of more than sixty copies known. The tablets and fragments belong mainly to the sixth and seventh centuries B.C. but there is evidence that the chief ideas in the legends themselves go back to the time of Abraham or even earlier. Although such a date would put those legends before the time of Moses this is of little importance, for it is equally probable that the substance of the first chapters of Genesis was known to Noah.

It is, however, on the overwhelming internal evidence that any theory of Jewish borrowing from Babylonian and Assyrian legends must be rejected. The alleged resemblances between Genesis 1 and the Babylonian legends could best be compared with the resemblances between a cathedral and a pigsty. It is true that, in the nature of the case, there must be a few resemblances; the cathedral and the pigsty both have walls, a roof and a door and even an architect! The two accounts we are considering both divide the story into seven sections, mention the stars, the moon and the ocean and give an account of the making of man. Even in these cases, however, the two accounts are so utterly different as to preclude any possible borrowing. The Babylonian account is a clumsy, confused and utterly debased story of squabbles between fabulous gods and monsters. But what has not often been sufficiently recognised is that these legends arose from confused myths and recollections of the two great acts of human rebellion against God, the first of which brought the Flood, and the second of which is associated with the Tower of Babel. It is from the 'heroes of these olden times' . . . these 'Men of renown' . . . that heathen religion has derived its gods and it is the purpose of the Babylonian legend to take the work and attributes of the True God and to attribute them to Marduk. Thus Tubal-cain, Noah, Ham, Cush, Nimrod and others have become merged into the Babylonian pantheon. As is the case in many heathen religions the chief god is by no means the oldest; he has parents and grandparents often into a remote past, showing that these gods are mainly derived from times after the Flood with vague recollections of ancestors going back many generations. Thus Marduk himself, the hero of 'Enuma Elish' the chief Babylonian 'creation' story, is son of Ea who was son of Anu. Anu, the 'sky god', had once been regarded as chief of the gods but even he was not the first, for he was son of a brother-sister pair, Anshar and Kishar, who were themselves children of Apsu and Tiamat.

The view that Genesis 1 is derived from the Babylonian tablets has until quite recently been held so widely and so dogmatically that many do not realise that it must be completely abandoned. It may, therefore, be useful to devote a little more time to the consideration of this point.

The Genesis account opens with that masterpiece of simplicity and profundity 'In the beginning God created the heaven and the earth', and then goes on to describe the coming of light to dispel the darkness that surrounded the great deep. The first Babylonian tablet does not directly mention the creation of heaven or earth and it says nothing of the coming of light. It tells how, before heaven and earth existed, Apsu (water) and his wife Tiamat (?ocean) had children like Mummu, Anshar and Kisher (brother and sister) and Lahmu and Lahamu (who might possibly be gods of the sun and moon). These children are described as tall (possibly a recollection of the nephilim of Genesis Chapter 5) and as living to a great age (Tablet 1 line 13). Anshar begat Anu and Anu begat Ea who was the father of Marduk. It is clear that in other variations of these legends these gods had other names and it is a difficult task to trace out their connections with the deities of other heathen religions. The tablet tells of Tiamat's decision to destroy all the younger gods (surely a debased recollection of God's threat to destroy the rebels of Genesis 5 by a Flood) and of Marduk's coming as a champion for the gods on condition that he is to be supreme among them.

The second stage of the Creation account in Genesis 1 tells of the formation of the atmosphere to separate the clouds from the ocean. The second Babylonian tablet describes how Tiamat, assisted by a brood of monsters (who might possibly be signs of the Zodiac), prepares to do battle, and how Marduk demands that the gods shall proclaim his supremacy.

In the third tablet, after much discussion about Tiamat's preparations, the gods arrange a feast and get drunk. 'Their bodies swelled as they drank the strong drink.'

'Exceedingly carefree were they, their spirit was exalted;
For Marduk, their avenger, they decreed the destiny.'

(Last three lines of Tablet 3).

I leave it to others to find any connection between this and the third day of Genesis 1.

In the fourth tablet Marduk fights with Tiamat and slays her, cutting her body in half and forming the sky out of half her body. He also takes prisoner her horde of demon followers (Tablet 4, line 116) and 'casts them into fetters'. There is here, of course, one tiny resemblance to Genesis 1 in that the sky is made by Marduk out of the ocean (Tiamat), and in Genesis there are waters above the firmament as well as below. But we shall see that there is no real similarity. The sky of Genesis 1 is not the clouds but the vast firmament, only a small part of which is below the clouds, the greater part extending far above into the remotest depths of space. Whether in the imprisonment of the demon hordes we have some vague recollection of the angels who fell and whose fate is recorded in 2 Peter 2. 4, and Jude 6 as being kept in bonds and cast into Tartarus (R.V. margin) until the day of Judgment, I do not pretend to know. The ancient records of Genesis 6 seem plainly to indicate that fallen spirit-beings had something to do with the great revolt which caused the Flood and had something to do with the heroes of old time, the men of renown, who are the heroes of Babylonian and Assyrian mythology.

The fifth tablet does not seem to fit easily into the series. It seems intended to show that Marduk determined the signs of the zodiac and appointed the phases of the moon. No doubt this was of significance in a religion where the Moon-goddess played so important a part, but it has no connection with the fifth day of Genesis 1 which deals with bird and marine life.

It is in the sixth tablet, where Marduk makes Man, that some have supposed the closest correspondence between the Babylonian and the Genesis accounts. Yet here careful study reveals the most amazing differences, and the Babylonian text again reveals its true connection, not with Creation, but with the post-Flood story of Babel.

In the sixth tablet Marduk, at the suggestion of Ea, gets the gods to kill the rebel god Kingu, and from his blood they make man, whose task is to wait on them while they rest. This being finished Marduk divides the gods into ranks and they, in return for his work for them, build him a temple which is none other than Esagila—'made of bricks and with its head on high' (lines 60-61). Here we have so plainly the Tower of Babel that no further proof is needed that 'Enûma Elish', far from being the Babylonian original of Genesis, is nothing more than a crude polytheistic heathen perversion of the events which took place in this world just before and just after the Flood.

The seventh tablet simply contained a number of the titles of Marduk, who was endowed by the other gods with all the titles and attributes of the One True God; thus blasphemously did the Evil One, all those centuries ago, succeed in turning the truth of God into a lie. So the evil one deceived the vast masses of mankind in the ancient world. From that vast tissue of lies sprang the heathen religions of old times . . . but it is surely almost unbelievable that he should have deceived even modern Christian critical scholars into believing that this was the original account from which the Hebrew writers later derived Genesis I. How subtle are the ways of him who said, 'Yea, hath God said?'

Little remains to be said of the numerous other tablets and fragments which represent many variations of the Babylonian account. As in most ancient writings, traces of the truth, twisted and distorted under a pile of polytheistic lies, can be discerned. There is no point in following them through long and tedious studies. The outcome is exactly the same as before. Not one of them has any possible claim to be the original that lies behind Genesis I. Not one adds one single thought of value to that great masterpiece which God has given us. Genesis I stands alone in its simplicity, its purity and its grandeur, owing nothing to the darkness of heathen night!

We turn with relief from this study of heathenism which seems to leave the mind and intellect—as all contact with heathenism does to the sensitive Christian spirit—tired and polluted. Yet before we can proceed with the delightful task of studying Genesis I in detail we have one more objection to meet. It is that of some modern scientists expressed perhaps most dogmatically by Prof. Fred Hoyle.

The ancient Jews, according to this argument, had such a primitive idea of the universe, so immeasurably inferior to ours, that we can derive nothing of value from Genesis I, nor is the Hebrew conception of God of any value in our day and generation.

The beauty of a picture does not depend on the appreciation of it held by one group of observers. Schoolboys often have a very inferior conception of the greatness of Shakespeare. The value of a poem or of a scientific treatise is not to be judged alone by the outlook or opinions of its first readers. If the poem touches reality, if the scientific treatise rests upon facts, its value will grow as human understanding grows. That is just what has happened with Genesis 1. It is a work which touches reality and rests upon facts. The wonderfully simple words have been so carefully chosen as to allow for almost unlimited expansion. The great truths which are enshrouded in its simple terms are true against the background of absolute truth irrespective of the varying appreciation of many generations and tens of millions of readers. It remains true that God created heaven and earth whatever shape people may have imagined for that earth, or whatever extent they assigned to that heaven.

If we today thank the astronomers for a conception of a Universe literally millions of millions of times as big as that conceived by the early Jews—then we thank them for enhancing our view of the greatness of Genesis 1 and of the Creator whose word is there recorded. Genesis 1 is true, irrespective of men's understanding of it. It is true even though we may err in our appreciation of it. As our knowledge of truth increases so does our appreciation of Genesis 1.

Having pursued our course through the dark tunnels of heathenism and doubt let us turn to the glorious light of the Book itself, and seek in the pages of Creation Revealed something of the wonders of Creation Planned.

CHAPTER 4

THE BEGINNING OF GENESIS 1

'In the beginning God created the heaven and the earth'
Gen. 1. 1

IF the story of Genesis 1 is the beginning of a story that proceeds unbroken to Revelation 22, and if into these 31 verses there are compressed the essentials of age-long processes that affected the wide expanses of earth and sky and sea, processes whose full description would require more books than this world has yet seen, how much more amazing in its simplicity, its comprehensiveness and its concentration is this first verse . . . the beginning of the beginning.

One's first impression of this verse is its amazing simplicity. A long time ago God created His universe.

A little girl pauses while playing with her doll's house to ask, 'Mummie, where did my doll's house come from?' 'Daddy made it years ago for your sister', is the simple answer. 'He painted the outside and papered the inside and made the furniture for it: some of the things have been broken by your brothers and sisters, but it was lovely when Daddy had finished it.' And the little girl pauses, thinks for a while of the wonder of a daddy who could make such a doll's house, and then goes on happily with her game, satisfied that she knows all that she needs to know about the making of her doll's house.

So God answers His children. It is still a wonderful world although we and our brothers and sisters have spoilt and broken some of it. It was wonderful when God finished it. And if we ask the same question, 'Where did it come from?' we have the same simple answer, 'Our heavenly Father made it a long time ago'.

That is all we need to know. Perhaps it is all that we can know. Yet the verse, with all the realities which it summarises, has always intrigued the mind of man.

The little girl grows up, and observes that the furniture of her doll's house belongs to an earlier fashion and style than that of the furniture which she and her husband have just bought for their new home. By a simple calculation from the age of her elder sister she deduces that the doll's house must have been made at least thirty years ago . . . but the old statement made by her mother still remains true . . . 'Daddy made it a long time ago'.

So man, searching among the rocks which surround his home has found stones and fossils which belong to an earlier age. By various calculations, not always very simple, he has tried to deduce how long ago these early ages may have been. Man would like to know just when God created the heaven and the earth.

I think that we do not know. I think we may never know, at least in this life. I am not sure that we fully understand the meaning of the question. I am not sure that we have even grasped all that is involved in the simple verse before us.

Let us, then, study the verse to try to determine what it means . . . not in its primary meaning, the very simplicity of which has staggered us, but against the background of the science we know, or think we know. Let us study it, not in the light of what the early Hebrews may have thought it meant, nor along the lines of fondly-held traditions, but against the background of such aspects of reality as we sincerely believe we have at last begun to discern. Let us see if its simple terms embrace a deeper meaning, a meaning that can run parallel to our mid-twentieth century conception of the Universe. Let us encourage ourselves with the realisation that in this life the most delightfully simple statements usually turn out to be the most profound, and finally let us realise that if we fail in our search we shall lose nothing, but shall return to the simple, all-important meaning of the verse: that God, the God of the rest of the Bible, created His Universe a long time ago.

In commencing our study of Genesis 1. 1 we are confronted with three possible translations of the first few verses. The first of these would make verse 1 stand in grand isolation, a statement complete in itself.

v. 1. In the beginning God created the heaven and the earth.

Verse 2 would then follow historically but with no clue as to how long a time had elapsed since the process of creation commenced.

> v. 2. And the earth was (in those early days)
> without form and void.

A variation which supposes that the earth *became* waste and void will also have to be considered.

The second translation[1] would make verse 1 a mere time-note introductory to verse 2. It would read:

> v. 1. When God began to create the heaven and the earth,
> v. 2. the earth was without form and void.

The third translation would make verse 1 a mere time-note for verse 3 as though the coming of light was the all-important opening step in the story. It would read:

> v. 1. In the beginning of God's creation of heaven and earth.
> v. 2. (when the earth was waste and void and darkness was
> upon the face of the deep, and the Spirit of God was
> hovering on the face of the waters).
> v. 3. God said 'Let there be light and there was light'.

The second and third translations have nothing like the simplicity and dignity of the first. They are possible paraphrases of what may be supposed to have been the thoughts of the writer and each is defended by a small number of Hebrew scholars. But they do not seem to do justice to the constant repetition of *waw* and they seem strangely out of keeping with the whole pattern and marvellous brevity of expression which characterize this chapter. While, of course, they still imply quite clearly that God created the universe, they no longer state it so emphatically as the great foundation truth on which all else must rest.

The first translation, with which our Authorised Version and the Revised Version both commence, accords more easily with the balancing phrase which closes the account in Genesis 2. 1 'Thus the Heaven and the Earth were finished and all the host of them'.

We shall keep, then, to that simple and dignified translation of verse 1 with which we have been familiar for so long and which still has the support of the majority of Hebrew scholars.

But translation is only the first step: it must be followed by

---

[1] Heidel, *Babylonian Genesis* considers this translation very fully but rejects it. On the other hand it is accepted by the new translation of the *Jewish Publication Society of America*.

interpretation. The first point of attack must be the phrase 'Heaven and Earth'. Here we are confronted with the phenomenon that both of these words have two meanings, not only in modern English, but also in the original Hebrew. We may speak of earth as distinct from sea, or we may speak of the planet. The word has a smaller as well as a larger meaning. We may speak of the birds of heaven, or of the stars of heaven. The word has a smaller and also a very much larger meaning.

This phenomenon will repay a little careful thought, for we shall find it again in the chapter, and it shows that we are dealing with the very early days of language itself. In the early days of human history men had to learn, as we always learn best, by proceeding from the known to the unknown, from the lesser to the greater, from the simple to the complex. Hence words had to extend their meanings.

Man stood upon solid ground. To him this substance which he called 'earth' was safe and hard and very different from sea. He knew which was which and he knew the difference quite well. When God, in His inspired account of Creation, wishes to use a word to describe the entire planet He extends the meaning of the word 'earth'—and *not* of the word sea. The planet itself is made of rocks and ores. It is made of silicates and oxides of aluminium and magnesium and compounds of calcium and of iron . . . hard, solid things. Even though it may be hot within, as a whole it possesses a remarkable rigidity. Thus the inspired account utterly repudiates the ideas of early heathen philosophers that the planet floats like a saucer on a limitless ocean.

There are numerous other evidences in Genesis that words had to be given extended meanings, but we are concerned now with only one. The word heaven could be used of the atmosphere or space around man in which he could move and birds could fly. It was very thin, almost 'empty stuff', so thin that the Bible often speaks of heaven as stretched out like a curtain. In the Hebrew it is given as a plural with the form of the dual—a form used by the Hebrews for that which was extended. We shall trace a similar thought of thinness in the term 'firmament' which is another word whose meaning is extended in the same chapter. Thus the inspired writer chooses the terms which could best be used of our atmosphere, for when solids and liquids turn to gases they become finer than any curtain; thin, almost 'empty stuff'

compared with solids. A pint of water gives over 1600 pints of
steam! But just as the word 'earth' was used for the little plot of
land on which man stood, and then for the whole planet, so the
word 'heaven' was used not only for the 'almost empty' space
above us in which the birds fly, but by extension, for the vast
realms of space beyond in which move countless hosts of stars.

All this is amazingly accurate. Space is not quite empty. It is
filled with the finest of material. Between the stars is the fine
interstellar matter—far less dense than air. Between the great
star groups is the still more extended intergalactic matter thousands
of times finer than the lightest gas on earth. God could not teach
early man all this but He just showed him that space is *not* made
of solid crystal (as some critics vainly suppose) but space—
heaven—is but a vast extension of that 'almost emptiness' that
man already knew. There is no solid dome of heaven with stars
stuck to its floor in Genesis 1. They exist in Genesis 1, as Sir
James Jeans and others discovered thousands of years later, in a
'stretched out' heaven, an 'expanded Universe'.

There are two more points to note. The term 'heaven and
earth' to the Hebrews has come to mean 'everything'—the
Universe. Secondly the expression occurs in several other places
and plainly refers, not to the immediate atmosphere of this little
world, but to the whole of space.

Gen. 2. 1 Thus the heavens and the earth were finished and all the
host of them.
Ps. 8. 3 When I consider the heavens, the work of Thy fingers,
The moon and the stars, which Thou hast ordained . . .
Neh. 9. 6 Thou Lord hast made the heaven, the heaven of heavens,
with all their host.

We can, then, interpret Genesis 1. 1 only as a sublime statement,
incomprehensible in its greatness, yet fully consistent with our
human understanding; too deep to fathom, yet absolutely
reasonable; a statement complete in itself that 'In the beginning
of the story, God, the God of the rest of the Book, created the
Universe'.

On this great monolith the rest of the Bible stands. If this one
verse is not true the whole of the Book is false! Science can find
no satisfactory alternative. The Christian, and many a scientist
is here included, accepts the statement by faith. There is only

one Ultimate Reality, only one Ultimate Being. The Universe is not eternal,[1] it is not self-existing. It was created by God. The remainder of the Bible sweeps away polytheism; this verse repudiates pantheism. The great foundation of all truth is laid in this verse. The great stellar universe is but the creature of the One Creator. The verse is not limited to our local soil and atmosphere, nor is it a mere adverbial phrase of time. It is the foundation stone on which all else is built.

We have travelled far in thought and have returned to the simple interpretation that springs to the mind of the simplest reader: in the beginning God created the Universe.

We have got back to our starting point but our time has not been wasted. In establishing the wider meaning of 'heaven and earth' we have enhanced beyond conception the greatness of the other terms in the first verse. We can now draw on all the truths revealed by all the modern astronomers and pack them all into this verse. God is now the Creator, not merely of one tiny planet less than 8,000 miles in diameter, but of a Universe whose extent defies measurement in millions of light years, Creation now is not merely the process of fashioning one little planet from pre-existing matter but the process of bringing into existence the very galaxies themselves. And the beginning is no longer the beginning of human history nor of this planet but—whatever the words can mean—of the Universe as we now know it. But what is more important than all, God is no longer the God of one tiny piece of matter which we call the Earth; He is the Creator of millions of stars stretching away into the remotest depths of space. In such proportion as the modern astronomers have enriched our conception of 'heaven and earth' beyond that of the Hebrews, by so much should our generation have increased our conception of the greatness of God.

Early or simple readers may see less, scientific readers may see more in Genesis 1. 1 . . . but the verse is true for both. It is true against the background of absolute truth; true whether we grasp its full meaning or not. We are profoundly indebted to the scientists for filling out the meaning of the terms, but we are profoundly indebted to God alone for the verse.

---

[1] i.e. in the sense that God is the Eternal (Jehovah). The Universe doubtless transcends Time in our limited conception and hence is eternal in the sense of 'aionian'.

We have set ourselves the task of looking at this verse against the background of modern science. We will not turn back although we now have some glimpse of the vastness of the project, but before we commence this herculean task let me repeat the warning: the verse is very, very simple. God wrote it and we could not have written it better. It means

A very long time ago
God created the Universe.

CHAPTER 5

THE HEAVENS

'In the beginning God created the heaven and the earth' Gen. 1. 1
(In Hebrew, seven words)

THE Bible is the story of one race of beings on one planet. It is
not the story of the Universe. Yet from time to time the writers
gaze at the story of the earth in its wider setting. The story has a
relation to God's vaster scheme—the heavens. This little story is
part of a greater cosmic story. Yet we shall not expect the book
to tell us very much about the deeper recesses of space or the
vaster reaches of time. What it does tell us, if we understand it
rightly, will be true. It will use simple words and beautiful figures
of speech easy enough for the humblest nomad to grasp. It will
show us, if we read far enough, that these simple words are
capable of vaster meanings and that they were carefully selected
for such use in Genesis, and so handled by later writers that their
latent significance can be discerned by the careful thinker.

We ask first then, 'What does the Bible tell us of the Heaven—
the Universe?' And the simple answer is this. 'It is not eternal,
it was created. It is vast in extent, fine in texture and it is studded
with unnumbered hosts of stars.' Let us consider these against
the background of modern science.

The Heaven—the Universe—is vast. A psalmist sat meditating
one day on the mercy of God. At that moment it seemed to him
so great that he searched for some comparison. Even the earth
seemed great to him and east seemed far from west, and he said
of God:

> 'As far as the east is from the west,
>   So far hath He removed our transgressions from us.'

But he wanted a vaster picture yet for the mercy of God and so
he wrote:

> 'For as the heaven is high above the earth,
>   So great is His mercy toward them that fear Him.'
>   Psalm 103, 11 and 12.

34

The heaven was so high—he could think of nothing higher—
that he used it as an illustration of the mercy of God. To the
psalmist heaven was high. We have an even greater conception of
the 'height' of the starry heaven, and surely too, if we measure
the mercy of God by the depth of Christ's descent to the Cross,
an even greater conception of God's mercy.

The greatest of the Old Testament prophets sat one day
recording the burning messages which poured through his mind
under the Spirit's influence. 'Thus saith Jehovah', he wrote:

> 'My thoughts are not your thoughts,
>   Neither are your ways My ways.
> For as the heavens are higher than the earth,
>   So are My ways higher than your ways,
>   And My thoughts than your thoughts.'
>
> Isa. 55. 8, 9

The comparison, if we may dare to take it mathematically, is this:
God's way is to man's way as heaven is to the earth. Isaiah may
not have realised fully the boldness of the metaphor but it is
there plainly enough for all to see. The heaven is incomparably
greater than the earth. The Bible teaches a universe so vast as to
defy measurement. And Science . . . ? The earth is one small
planet some 7,900 miles in diameter set in a path about 93 million
miles from a star which we call our sun, an object over 333,000
times as massive as our planet. This star is one of a galaxy or
collection of stars numbering some thousands of millions and
extending possibly over an area of space measured in terms of
something like 100,000 light years across—and each light year is
6 million million miles. And this galaxy is but one of millions of
such galaxies scattered at distances of a million light years apart
into the remotest depths of space. How vast indeed is God's
Universe; how wonderful the Creator of such a Heaven! Yet
Isaiah was right. God's ways are as much greater than man's ways
as Heaven is greater than Earth. The truth of the ratio still holds.
The Universe, according to the Bible and according to modern
science, is a very large place!

Vast in its extent, innumerable in its hosts! So the Bible
teaches—and modern science agrees. Let us examine first what
the Bible has to say about the number of stars. We shall not
expect the answer to be given as a precise mathematical expression

but, seeing that the book is intended for ordinary folk, as some
figure of speech or comparison with something well known.

The account of the Creation finishes with the short passage
(Gen. 2. 1) which is parallel to the opening sentence (Gen. 1. 1),
'And the heaven and the earth were finished and all the host of
them'. All the *host* of heaven! The Hebrew word (*tsaba'*) was
derived from the idea of gathering forces for an army. It was
always intended to represent a large number. There might be
within the army individual groups, for we read of captains of
tens, of hundreds and of thousands, but the entire company was
the *host*. The 'hosts' of Israel and Assyria frequently exceeded a
hundred thousand. But the Hebrews also believed that God had
His hosts.

> 'Bless the Lord, ye angels of His,
>   Ye mighty in strength, that fulfil His word,
> Bless the Lord, all ye His *hosts*;
>   Ye ministers of His, that do His pleasure.'
>
> Ps. 103. 20-21 (R.V.)

God is, in fact, constantly regarded as *Lord of Hosts*, and to
Daniel in his vision (Dan. 7. 10) it was revealed that that angelic
host numbered more than a hundred million.

A host then could be a very large number. Perhaps to later
readers of the Bible its very meaning has grown larger. But God
told Abram that his descendants would be like the stars of heaven
and like the sand of the sea for multitude! Are the two metaphors
comparable? Can we compare the few thousands of stars which
Abram might count on a clear night with the myriad measures of
sand on the sea shore? Can we even compare those few thousands
of visible stars with the tens of millions of descendants of Abram
who have actually lived to prove the truth of God's promise?
Can we—or was there buried in the very simile itself the possibility
of an expanding meaning as the human race progressed?

In Jeremiah 33. v. 22 we have the position stated even more
clearly.

> 'As the *host* of Heaven cannot be numbered,
>   Neither the sand of the sea measured;
> So will I multiply the seed of David my servant,
>   And the Levites that minister unto me.'

God has indeed promised that through the work of 'Great
David's greater Son' He will raise up an innumerable company

of those who will be both sons and ministers, but it is the first part of the simile that attracts our attention. The Host of Heaven can no more be numbered than can the sand of the seashore be measured.

Can they be numbered? Go out on to a hill top on a clear moonless night. The stars seem to stretch away into the remotest depths of space. Tinier and tinier points of light sparkle as the eye travels around some well-known constellation. They certainly give the *impression* of being innumerable . . . and as such they provide a perfect simile for the prophetic comparisons. But the cold critic may press the point. The simile ought to be based on facts not just impressions. After all, the number of stars visible on a clear night can be estimated, and 10,000 would be a reasonable figure. Was Jeremiah wise to say the host of heaven could not be numbered?

Stars differ from one another in brightness or 'magnitude'. Some, such as Aldebaran, are described as 1st magnitude stars. A star of 6th magnitude is only 1/100th as bright as this and one of 11th magnitude is only 1/100th as bright as the 6th magnitude star. There are not many stars brighter than 1st magnitude but there are over 500 whose magnitude exceeds 4 and over 20,000 of magnitude up to 8. When telescopes are used the numbers can only be estimated from photographic plates. At magnitude 12 there are over a million and at magnitude 16, thirty-three million. By the time magnitude 21 is reached there are nearly 1,000 million. But we have now only just got going, for long before this the big telescopes have been picking up literally thousands of other star groups outside our own. These groups are themselves composed of hundreds of millions of stars and it is estimated that, but for certain factors which obscure the view to some extent, the 100-inch telescope would register 100 million of these groups! The Universe goes on far beyond that. The 200-inch telescope and the still more recent devices are revealing very many more groups far away in the depths of space, until we can speak of 1000 million galaxies each containing 1000 million stars—but we must leave it at that. Jeremiah was quite right when he said the host of heaven could not be numbered for multitude. He had been guided to use a phrase that was more true than he could have realised: a phrase that has held even in the light of modern scientific knowledge.

Vast in its extent, innumerable in its multitude, fine in its texture: such is the Bible's contribution to our knowledge of the Universe.

Expanded—stretched out like a curtain. As we have already observed the Hebrew word for heaven, *shamayim*, has the form of a dual but is actually a plural noun. This phenomenon occurs among words used for things which are extended. It occurs in the closely-related word for water or seas—*mayim*—that which is spread out over so much of the earth's surface. We have seen, too, that the word *shamayim* belongs to the class of words whose meaning has been enlarged. The word is used not only for the atmosphere but also for stellar space, and we shall see later that the associated word 'firmament', not only also carries a wider as well as a narrower meaning, but likewise implies that which is very fine in its texture.

Jeremiah, speaking of the Great Judge of nations (Jer. 51. 14-15), describes Him as the 'Lord of Hosts . . . He that made the earth by His power and stretched out the heaven by His understanding'. Isaiah, too, speaks of the One True God (Isa. 40) to whom nations are like the little trace of dust that renders a balance inaccurate or to whom even islands are but 'fine dust'. He it is who 'stretches out the heavens like a curtain (v. 22 R.V. margin 'gauze') and spreads them like a tent to dwell in'. A Universe like gauze! Again the prophet has been guided to a simile more wonderfully accurate than he could have realised. Even to the simple observer the heavens give the impression of amazing fineness of texture. But again it is not mere impression, it is scientific fact. Although the stars are huge in themselves they are so far apart that the average density of matter in the Universe is far below that of any gauze or curtain that man could make. The total mass of the Universe lies not so much in the stars themselves as in the interstellar and intergalactic matter and the density of this latter is of the order of 10^{-19} grams per cubic centimetre, or approx. 10^{-15} that of hydrogen. Professor Hoyle illustrated the fineness of the Universe by saying that the intergalactic matter would provide only one atom per matchbox of space!

Such then is the heaven of the Bible, of Genesis 1. 1, and such too is the heaven of modern science. Vast in its extent, innumerable in its host and remarkably fine in its texture.

CHAPTER 6

'GOD CREATED . . . '

BEFORE we turn to a consideration of the earth let us think for a while of the process by which these heavens of which we have just spoken came into being. Let us proceed with the greatest humility and caution, remembering the challenge of God to Job (Chapter 38. 2 R.V.):

> 'Who is this that darkeneth counsel
> By words without knowledge? . . .
> Gird up now thy loins like a man;
> For I will demand of thee, and declare thou unto Me.
> Where wast thou when I laid the foundations of the earth?
> Declare, if thou hast understanding. . . .'

If Job had no direct knowledge of the formation of this little earth how much less have we of the commencement of the universe!

We may ask then, very cautiously, two questions. Does the Bible throw any light on this process which it calls creation? Does modern science help?

I think that in both cases the answer is 'yes—a little'. A little—and then only if we are prepared to learn and not to approach the question with preconceived notions of how we think things ought to have happened.

It is always well worth while considering the different shades of meaning and different uses of Bible words that are otherwise somewhat similar to each other. If we consider a verse like Isaiah 45. 18 (R.V.):

> 'For thus saith the Lord that *created* the heavens;
>   He is God;   that *formed* the earth
>   and *made* it;
>   He   *established* it,
>   He *created* it not a waste,
>   He *formed* it to be inhabited . . .'

39

we see at once that we are involved in the study of four words: create, form, make and establish. They are not very easy to define, and to some extent they overlap. The verb *'asah* 'to make' is the simplest. It is just the common word for 'make' or 'do' such as we have in our own language. The Bible provides many examples of its use:

> Noah made an ark
> The Israelites made bricks
> Bezaleel made the tabernacle
> The Lord made heaven and earth
>   (Exodus 20. 11).

There is no particular emphasis here on the verb. One's attention rests for a moment equally upon each word: Noah, made, ark. Quite evidently the word *bara'* 'to create' is a greater word than *'asah* and includes the lesser term within its scope.

The verb 'to establish' used in Isaiah 45. 18 comes from the Hebrew *kun*. This word is sometimes translated 'to prepare' and sometimes 'to establish'. The former meaning is clear in such passages as

> Gen. 43. 16   Joseph said, Slay and *make ready*; for these men shall dine with me at noon.
> Exod. 16. 5   And it shall come to pass that on the sixth day, they shall *prepare* that which they bring in.
> Amos 4. 12   *Prepare* to meet thy God.

The second meaning is also common, for we read that a house (Judges 16. 26; Micah 4. 1), a throne (1 Kings 2. 45), a kingdom (1 Kings 2. 12), and even a heart (Ps. 112. 7) can be *established*. In Jeremiah 10. 12 we read:

> He hath made the earth by His power,
> He hath *established* the world by His wisdom.

The force of the verb *kun*, then, as used in the Old Testament is clearly to make something ready beforehand, with a purpose in view, i.e. to prepare, and to do it so completely that no subsequent alterations are necessary, i.e. to stabilize or establish. Thus, as Jeremiah 10. 12 says, it requires power to *make* something, but it requires wisdom to *prepare* it perfectly for some preconceived task. Isaiah 45. 18 tells us that God established the earth. He prepared it completely with an object in view—He created it not, He says, to be empty, but to be inhabited.

The third of the four words used in Isaiah 45. 18 is 'to form'. The Hebrew *yatsar* means 'to form or fashion', and it is often used for the potter. Here then our attention rests on the actual process of making or shaping. A potter works quickly and the onlooker is impressed by his wonderful skill, but the work is not instantaneous, it grows—it is a process with various stages—and the clay passes from the formless state to the beautifully-formed condition. It is what in modern scientific terms might be called a 'disorder to order transformation'. But it does not arise by itself. The form or pattern does not originate in the clay, it originates in the mind of the potter. So also the 'form' or 'image' of this Universe did not originate in the matter but in the mind of God. Here it is interesting to note that the closely allied word *yetser* means imagination or thought, i.e. a mental pattern or image. Inasmuch then as the word *create* is used alongside the verb *to form*—and it is twice bracketed with it in Isaiah 45. 18—it implies that creation can be a process of forming or fashioning something to a preconceived pattern which is external to itself.

But what then is the central idea of the actual word *create*? The Hebrew *bara'* is of somewhat obscure origin. In its simple form it means 'to cut'. In Joshua 17. 18 we read 'It is a wood, and thou shalt *cut it down*'. But this use of *bara'* is rare, and it is plainly one of those words whose meaning has been extended. In its main sense it is never used of anyone but God. When used as a noun it means the Creator Himself, as we see in Ecclesiastes 12. 1 'Remember now *Thy Creator*' and in Isaiah 40. 28 '*The Creator* of the ends of the earth'. Yet, like *kun* and *yatsar*, it adds something to the meaning of *'asah* to make, and the clue to this additional force can be found in several different verses.

Exod. 34. 10 'I will do marvels, such as have not *been done* (*bara'*) in all the earth.'
Num. 16. 30 'But if the Lord make a new thing' (create a creation).
Isa. 48. 6-7 'I have showed thee new things . . . they are created now . . .'
Isa. 65. 17 'For, behold, I create new heavens and a new earth. . . .'

Bara', then, adds to *'asah*, to make, the force of something new, something which did not exist as such before. But the question arises as to whether the word implies the instantaneous production of a finished article from nothing. Here we have two questions. Does *bara'* imply an instantaneous act? Plainly, no. In Genesis 1. 27 we read 'male and female created He them' . . . but Eve was created after Adam. Further, all men are described as *created* by God (Gen. 6. 7; Ps. 89. 47; Ecc. 12. 1). God *created* the whole race. In Ps. 102. 18 we read of a people which shall be *created*. The verb in itself, then, gives no clue as to time. It simply asserts that what was created had not existed as such before. The verb *kun*, to prepare beforehand, to make ready, to establish, and *yatsar* to form or fashion as a potter, give us the answer to the question of the time involved.

But does *bara'* imply creation from nothing? Again the answer must be, 'Not necessarily'. Adam was created, not from nothing, but from 'the dust'. Eve was created, not from nothing, but from Adam. Creation is not necessarily from nothing, yet in verse 1 the word is used to assert that there was a time when this Universe as we now know it did not exist. The Universe *as such* is not eternal. The position is put most clearly in the words of Hebrews 11. 3 'Through faith we understand that the worlds (ages, aeons) were framed (prepared, perfected) by the word of God, so that things which are seen were not made of things which do appear'. Beyond this the Bible does not go, for the simple reason that beyond this the human mind cannot go. The material universe was made from something non-material which was in itself the production of 'word', the absolute, final, creative power of the One who alone is uncreate, the *eternal*.

There is, however, yet one more thought before we sum up the Bible teaching about Creation. This is not the only creation. It is in fact already growing old. The Bible is emphatic that a new creation—admittedly of a different order—has already commenced. The Bible asserts that when Christ rose from the dead He became the Head of a new creation. When human beings accept Him as Saviour and Lord they become 'new creatures'— part of a new creation. The old order will grow older. The new will expand until at last, as the prophet foretold, there will be a new heaven and a new earth, and this age, the brief aeon of man's existence, will be lost sight of in the New Age. The New Creation is taking shape; God is creating it; it is new; He is preparing and establishing it; it has a purpose and it will never be moved. He is forming and fashioning it like a Potter; His people are the clay and the vessels take long to shape—but one day it will be finished, a New Creation.

So much, then, can we learn from the Bible about the creation of the Universe. God made it all (*'asah*). He created it (*bara'*). It had never existed as such before. The material universe was made from the non-material, which in its turn was the product of the creative *word* of God (Heb. 11. 3). The work had a purpose (*kun*). It was prepared beforehand for the tasks its Creator had planned and it was established so that it needed no constant alterations. It involved the careful forming and fashioning of the Divine Potter (*yatsar*) to bring it to the form of that pattern or plan which arose, not in matter, but in the mind of God Himself. Such then is implied by the Bible as it fills out for us the meaning of those seven great words:

'In the beginning God created the heaven and the earth.'

We come now to the second of our questions concerning the process called creation. Does modern science help? Once again I think the answer is 'Yes—a little'.

For a very long time now man has speculated on the nature and origin of matter. Almost all the early philosophers suggested that the material world was derived from a few 'first principles' or elements. Sometimes these were identified with the oceans or with the sun; frequently they were personified and merged into the heathen pantheons. Many thinkers attributed the material universe to a combination of two opposing principles, light and darkness, or fresh water and salt water, or ether and air. Others, like Greek thinkers, who were certainly influenced by the views of still earlier philosophers, propounded theories of a single primal substance as, for example, water or fire. In the fifth and fourth centuries B.C. much attention was given to the nature and origin of matter. On the whole the view prevailed that matter was composed of a few simple 'elements' like earth, air, fire, water and possibly a fifth 'essence', ether. Many philosophers held that all matter was composed of small, very hard particles which could never be divided and hence were called atoms. The origin of this view is lost in obscurity. It was part of the foundation of the teaching of Epicurus whose followers became known as the

Epicureans. But Epicurus seems certainly to have derived it from Democritus of Abdera who in turn owes something to the little-known philosopher Leucippus. Some ancient writers trace the atomic theory back even further to a philosopher whose name is given as Mochus or Moschus, who was probably a Phoenician and who may have lived before 1000 B.C. Be that as it may, the atomic theory became widespread by the fourth century B.C. and seeing that atoms could not be divided they were regarded as eternal. Many of the Greek thinkers argued that coming into being was impossible and they therefore concluded that matter was eternal. The multitudinous substances in the Universe only existed because of the inconceivably vast number of ways in which atoms could be arranged. Atoms themselves could neither be created nor destroyed.

Sir Isaac Newton wrote: 'It seems probable to me, that God in the beginning formed matter in solid, massy, hard, impenetrable, moveable particles; . . . incomparably harder than any porous bodies compounded of them; even so very hard, as never to wear or break in pieces; no ordinary power being able to divide what God Himself made One, in the first creation.' (Works, 1782, IV. 260).

This view survived until the present century. While it remained, science could not get one step nearer to an appreciation of creation. The law of the conservation of matter seemed absolute. The most careful weighings showed that during chemical reaction no appreciable change in mass could be detected. Yet modern scientists were convinced that the 'law' is not ultimately true. The changes were simply too small for the balances to record. Matter can be destroyed and matter can be created. But when it is 'destroyed' it does not cease to exist. It travels out into space . . . as energy. Conversely, when some tiny portion of energy, some photon of light, ceases to exist as energy it appears to our reckoning as a small particle of matter. The two realities, matter and energy, are inextricably interwoven; to us the sum total seems to be conserved, but each can change into the other. The great starry host exist as such by turning matter into energy.

The creation of matter, then, which seemed absolutely impossible to generations of philosophers and scientists is no longer inconceivable. Matter can be made from energy. That which is visible has been made from that which 'does not appear'.

The ultimate problem still remains, and I think must remain, because it lies beyond the bounds of the human mind to solve, as to how God 'created' energy. Do we need to know? I think not. Just as a child grows tired of asking questions so the scientist is content that, at the far end of all his inquiries, there shall still remain one ultimate question unanswered. Somehow it seems fitting that it should be so. And it is there that many of us are prepared to put in the one final act of faith and to rest content. In the beginning God, our Father, created the Universe of energy and matter. We need not know how.

CHAPTER 7

THE EARTH

WE come next in our study of Genesis 1. 1 to the words 'the Earth'. It is a great descent from the starry heaven to a tiny planet, but in so far as the purpose of this Book centres upon this tiny Earth, it takes its rightful place in the opening verse of the Bible.

We have already commented on the fact that the Hebrew word *'erets* most commonly means 'land' or 'ground'. We read of the *'erets* of Canaan, of Moriah, of Egypt, of Goshen . . . all in the Book of Genesis. Abram was called to leave his own *'erets* and go to one which God would shew him. Yet it was this ordinary word for land which God used to describe the whole planet in Genesis 1. 1. The conception of the whole planet was thus brought before the Hebrew readers by extending the use of their word for solid land. How strange that in our own language the word *earth* (*ereth*) has still the double meaning of 'ground' and 'planet'. The connection is scientifically sound, for both are made of the same materials—largely metallic compounds, frequently silicates and aluminates.

Our insatiable curiosity immediately wants to know where this planet came from. The Bible, as we have seen, indicates that it was 'formed' and 'fashioned' with a definite purpose in view. Our mid-twentieth century science can add little to that.

Our planet is one of a group of approximately spherical objects which revolve around the sun in paths which are nearly circular. These objects vary in size from some, called minor planets, which are no more than spherical lumps of rock a few miles across, to the giant Jupiter whose volume is about 1300 times that of the earth. Their mean distances from the sun also vary widely, from the 35 million miles of Mercury to the 3,500 million of Pluto, and the years, in like manner, from the 88 days of Mercury to the 247 years of Pluto. Our earth is probably the densest, being $5\frac{1}{2}$ times as 'heavy' as water, while Saturn is actually less

46

dense than water or alcohol. So far as temperature is concerned it seems that the sun might maintain a temperature on the surface of Mercury nearly sufficient to melt solder while on Neptune or Pluto it seems likely that air could only exist at all as a liquid.

When we come to the question of the origin of these planets we have a number of facts and a selection of theories. Scientists have spent much time in calculating the exact paths of the planets, their mass and their angular momentum or spinning power. It has been found possible to make some deductions about their constitution and that of any gaseous atmosphere that surrounds them. The dark lines, and indeed many others, in the various spectra of the sun have been recorded with precision and traced to the elements involved. Meteorites pulled in from space by our planet in its journey have been carefully analysed. There are plenty of facts but at present no certain explanation that will fit them all.

In the eighteenth century various thinkers—we meet with names as far removed from each other as Emanuel Swedenborg, Thomas Wright of Durham and Immanuel Kant—considered the possibility of a vast condensing mass of gas revolving and throwing off portions which became planets while the residue became the central sun. This view was little more than a modification of the speculations of some of the Greek atomists. It was supported by Pierre Simon de Laplace in 1796, and became widely known as the nebula hypothesis. The great mathematician James Clerk Maxwell in 1859 showed that the theory was unsatisfactory but it remained popular for another fifty years.

With the present century new views grew up. Professors T. Chamberlain and F. R. Moulton supposed that a wandering star came near the sun and attracted 'bolts' of material from it and that these masses condensed to form planets. Sir James Jeans modified this view but still left it with many problems unsolved. Sir Harold Jeffreys tried a theory in which a wandering star secured a 'grazing hit' on the sun, while Dr. Lyttleton and Professor H. N. Russell considered that before the collision the sun might have been a binary star or 'pair' of suns close together.

Yet other theories considered the possibility of a wandering star approaching an unstable star either at the time when it was due to break up, or when, like the so-called 'Cepheid' stars it was due to increase greatly in size. Another theory attributed the origin of the solar system to the explosion of a giant star, or star pair, of the 'super nova' type, such as that which took place about 900 years ago in Cancer and became the Crab Nebula. One of the pair became the sun, the other receded far into space, leaving the planets as small fragments formed in the explosion.

Yet other astronomers have searched among the possibilities of a star wandering in an interstellar gas cloud and setting up eddies and vortices, or making use of its vast magnetic forces to produce ionised (electrically charged) clouds of particles which might coalesce to form planets. These planets, swinging in orbits in the sun's equatorial plane would themselves be electrically and magnetically charged and would accumulate matter to themselves until the whole region consisted only of a central sun and a relatively small number of planets. Those who are interested to follow the study further will find a fascinating account of the many theories mentioned above, in Professor W. M. Smart's book, The Origin of the Earth. The problems are intriguing; the suggested solutions are interesting but lacking in certainty, and for once the uncertainty seems so wide that, on this point, science can add nothing to the simple words of Genesis 1. 1, 'In the beginning God created ... the earth.' We have at present no idea how He did it.

CHAPTER 8

THE BEGINNING OF CREATION

OUR tour of the universe and of the first verse of Genesis 1 is nearly ended. One problem still remains. When did God create the heavens and the earth? When was the beginning?

The Hebrew word *bere'shith* gives its name to the first book in the Hebrew Scripture. Each book in the Pentateuch is named after the opening word. The word seems to be perfectly translated by our word 'beginning' and to imply no more than the English word does. If the Bible is to deal with a race of beings on this planet then it must surely *begin* with God's creating the earth on which later He put man. The word merely takes us back to that beginning and gives no clue as to the time in years. Elsewhere, however, in the Bible we do get hints that this beginning was a very long time ago. Not only have we the majestic statement of Psalm 90. 4 'A thousand years in Thy sight are but as yesterday when it is past', but the Hebrew writers several times hint at the great antiquity of the mountains. We read, for example, in Exodus 15. 18 that 'the Lord shall reign for ever *and ever*' and the same Hebrew word *'ad* is used in Hab. 3. 6 for the *everlasting* mountains. The Hebrew word *'olam* which is also used for *age-long* and which corresponds to the Greek aiōn, is used in Genesis 49. 26 for the 'utmost bounds of the *everlasting* hills'. Finally the curious word *qedem* which originally meant 'before' is used in Deuteronomy 33. 15 for the *ancient* mountains and in verse 27 for the *eternal* God. Without stressing too far these references to 'everlasting' hills we may safely conclude that the Hebrew scriptures regard the mountains as extremely ancient and as fitting symbols of that which endures for a very long time. But if we ask 'How long'—in terms of our years it seems to me that the Bible gives us no answer.

Can, then, science help us here? How old is the Universe? How old is the Earth?

We must first separate the two questions and then try to define the limits of each. The 'age of the Universe' must mean the number of years since it came into existence in a form at least something like that which we now perceive.[1] One line of approach might be to consider its rate of expansion. It seems to be expanding, although, with our present knowledge, it would not be safe to assert dogmatically that the peculiar shift of certain spectral lines usually so characteristic of a receding object, will never receive any other and, maybe, better explanation. But at present it seems to us that the Universe is expanding at a measurable rate; it has been said that 1,300 million years ago it was only half its present size. If that story could be repeated safely backwards for 13,000 million years it would be only $(\frac{1}{2})^{10}$ or about one-thousandth of its present size and similarly 26,000 million years ago it would have been but one-millionth its present diameter, and plainly the reasonable limit for its age would be set at a few more thousand million years. The rate of expansion might have —quite probably would have—changed with time. Even then, if the variation follows a mathematical law, and it undoubtedly does, it is still possible to form some idea of limiting age. Still it remains at best a somewhat hazardous procedure to carry a mathematical formula derived from a few years' observations, back over so vast a period. It is true that, on a much smaller scale, it has been observed that the Crab Nebula is expanding at a measurable rate and by a similar calculation it is concluded that it was caused by the explosion of a 'super-nova' type star about 800 years ago. Further, Chinese records do mention a new star seen in 1054 A.D. so bright as to be visible by day, which ought to have been true of so great an explosion. The agreement of the calculation, admittedly only approximate, of 800 years with the 900 thus provided by historical record suggest that such calculations are worthy of respect, but any scientist will agree that there is a great difference between a relatively straightforward problem like the age of the Crab Nebula and that of the age of our galaxy or of the Universe as a whole.

A second line of approach has been to consider the temperature of stars. It does seem possible that the stars might be formed as huge, low-density 'giants' some of which are thousands of times

---

[1] As distinct from the 'age of matter'. Prof. Hoyle would hold that no two atoms have the same age—they are born one by one.

bigger than our sun. They might contract to join the 'main sequence' of stars with surface temperatures of the order of 15,000°C and then cool down through that 'sequence' to, maybe, a mere 3,000°C. It would certainly take many thousands of millions of years to 'run down' the sequence, but this gives us no real clue as to the age of the Universe. Are the great giants newly-formed baby stars and are the 3,000°C stars old grandparents? If some stars 'blow up', do they all follow a history of decay and revival? There are serious attempts to answer these questions but the data seem insufficient. We know so little that we begin to see that even the question of the age of the Universe is probably a question to which there can be no one simple answer.

A third possible approach, rather from the 'other end' of the problem, so to speak, is to consider the distances of stars and nebulae. The sun is at a mean distance of about 93 million miles from the earth and hence its light reaches us in about 8 minutes. The Dog Star, Sirius, is much further away but its distance is known with considerable accuracy, and calculation shows that its light (and that of its small brother) reaches us in 8.6 years. When we come to the more remote stars it is necessary to make certain assumptions which are quite reasonable and which seem to yield consistent results, though admittedly detracting to that extent from absolute certainty. There can, however, be little doubt that the more remote stars of our own galaxy are of the order of 100,000 light years away. If we are right in concluding that the great Nebula in Andromeda is another such star galaxy as our own, but far outside it, then calculation shows that it must be some three-quarters of a million light years away. But the sky is dotted with nebulae that seem to be far more remote than the starry host of Andromeda. It seems that we must speak of the more distant star-cities as being many millions of light years away. Then slowly the strangeness of the position dawns upon us. If we see them today they must have been created millions of years ago for their light to reach us. But we spoke of the age of the Universe as being the time since it first had some form comparable to that which we now see. Yet we cannot see the Universe as it now is. We can only see Sirius as it was eight and a half years ago, and the Andromeda Nebula as it used to be three-quarters of a million years ago. Once again the very question itself seems to be running away from us.

What then is the verdict of science thus far? The stars are very old . . . many of them are doubtless thousands of millions of years old. But the question of the age of the Universe—or the so-called date of Creation—is at present a meaningless and unanswerable question. Hence the Bible makes no attempt to deal with such impossible questions but says all that need be said in the simple phrase 'In the beginning God created the Heavens'.

The second question also has its difficulties. Once again we are not clear as to the starting point when we speak of the age of the earth, especially as we are not certain as to how it was formed. All we can really do is to follow up certain clues. Some have attempted to determine the age of the oceans by calculating the amount of salt brought down by the rivers each year and figures varying from 20 million to 200 million years have been given. But we have little clue as to the rate of increase of saltness of the very early oceans. The very hot seas that we presume were first formed must have had a colossal weathering and leaching action upon the solids with which they came in contact. Other scientists have attempted to calculate how long it must have taken for the earth to cool—assuming that it was once molten—to its present temperature. The early results were inaccurate because they failed to allow for the 'warming' effects of the earth's radioactivity, and even now the facts and figures are difficult to interpret.

The ordinary observations of countless geologists were, however, of considerable force. Contemplation of the immense deposits of chalk or limestone at, say, Beachy Head or Cheddar Gorge, coupled with a study of the minute grain structure of these rocks and their fossils, some of which are smaller than a pin's head, compelled a belief in a vast stretch of time for the production of such rocks. The formation of a single seam of coal, to say nothing of those regions where more than a dozen such seams lie one above the other often separated by many feet of intervening deposits, all compelled belief in a time scale of millions of years.[1]

Into these various layers of rocks through great cracks and crevices there have come at times masses of molten rocks bearing compounds of the metals uranium and thorium. After they have

---

[1] See Dr. S. C. Curran *The Determination of Geological Age by means of Radio-activity. Chemical Society, Quarterly Reviews* 1953, VII No. 1 and Prof. F. E. Zeuner, *Dating the Past*. Henry M. Morris and John C. Whitcomb, Jr., in their book *The Genesis Flood* seek, rather unconvincingly, to cast doubts on all evidence for the great age of rocks.

settled down there they have continued, *in situ*, to change steadily into lead, each into its own particular type (or isotope) of lead and at a rate controlled by a logarithmic formula which is in some way a reflection of its own nuclear architecture and energy. In some rocks these compounds occurred only as minute specks and examination under the microscope of the tiny rings or haloes by which each is surrounded enables us to tell what substances were present and how long a 'life' each had. Attempts have been made to determine the age of the specks by the relative intensities of the rings. It is, however, much easier to determine the age of a rock by a relatively simple formula connecting the amounts of uranium and thorium and their respective lead isotopes present in each specimen. Thus some of the so-called tertiary rocks that might easily be contemporary with the London Clay give figures of the order of 50 million years; those of the 'secondary' period, an age when giant reptiles appeared, give ages nearly twice as great. Some of the carboniferous rocks of the 'primary' period give radio-dates of the order of 100 million to 200 million years and the Cambrian days beloved by the quaint trilobites must have been more like 500 million years ago. Some of the older pitchblendes and monazite sands, however, give indications of an age exceeding 1,500 million years. In recent times other quite different radio-active rocks have been analysed in a similar way, tracing the changes of radio-active potassium into argon and calcium, and radio-rubidium into strontium and although the results so far are few in number they provide a useful independent check, as they do not involve uranium or lead.

It would seem, then, that the present evidence suggests that great forests grew on this earth 200 million years ago, that vast oceans rose and fell with their daily tides more than 500 million years ago and that there were solid rocks beyond a 1,000 million years before that. We are not for the moment concerned with any attempts to be more precise. Beyond this the evidence grows fainter, but maybe the earth itself existed 2,000 million or 3,000 million years ago and thus is by no means a baby when compared with the age of our star group which itself may not be more than 6,000 million years old.

But to most of us the figures fail to convey any more meaning than just that of stupendous antiquity; yet they are consistent with all the other aspects of the Creator's work. A Universe of a thousand million galaxies each composed of a thousand million stars set at distances of thousands of million of miles surely requires comparable figures in time. To a Creator who deals with such vastnesses of space, miles and years must have a very different meaning from that which they have to us.

To use the words of the Psalmist, to Him a thousand years are no more than yesterday morning was to us; evening would bring a new era. The whole majestic picture as we have now surveyed it both from the Bible and from modern science is vast, consistent both in space and time, stupendous in its impressiveness. Yet lest the awful vastness of God's universe in space and time should overwhelm the thoughts of simple readers like ourselves, God, in His marvellous condescension, records all this incredibly stupendous work in those delightfully simple words from which we commenced and to which, for the last time, we return:

'In the beginning God created the heaven and the earth'.

CHAPTER 9

DARKNESS AND THE DEEP

'And the earth was without form and void, and darkness was
upon the face of the deep. And the Spirit of God moved upon
the face of the waters.'   Gen. 1. 2

FROM now onwards the story begins to narrow down its scope.
From the Universe we descend to a single planet. In Chapter 2
we narrow the study still further to one small zone of the Earth's
surface and, dismissing all other creatures, narrow the account
down to one race of beings—man. In later chapters the story
narrows still further to one family, the descendants of Jacob, and
finally with the gospels focusses all the attention on one Person,
Jesus Christ. From then on the scope widens once more—
Jerusalem, Judea, Samaria, Asia Minor, Greece, Rome. It widens
its scope to all nations and kindreds and tribes and looks at last
to a new creation—a new Heaven and a new Earth.

In verse 2 then the story narrows down from the Universe to
the Earth. This Earth we are told was at first uninhabited and in
fact uninhabitable. No difficulty exists here; it could hardly be
otherwise, for God had still much to do to prepare it for the
complicated organisms which were to live here.

For a short time we must turn aside to deal with another of
those unfortunate theories which have tended to obscure the
simple, majestic and orderly interpretation of Genesis 1. This
theory, generally called the Gap Theory, supposes that back in
'the beginning' the earth was inhabited by beings whose rebellion
against the Creator caused it to fall into a state of chaos, and
that the rest of Chapter 1 is not the story of creation but of the
restoration of a wrecked earth. Parts of this view seem to go
back to times before the Norman Conquest; Caedmon and King
Edgar[1] are mentioned in connection with it, but the alleged

_____

[1] See Bishop Wordsworth's *Commentary on Genesis* 1.

scientific aspects of it were developed about 1814 by the Scottish preacher Dr. Chalmers.[1]

The theory maintains the following postulates:

1. That since everything which God does is perfect, the earth in Gen. 1. 1 must have been perfect. Seeing that in verse 2 it is not perfect some evil being must have wrecked it.

2. That in Isa. 45. 18 God says that He did not create the world in vain (R.V. waste). Hence it was not waste and void in the beginning as verse 2 says, but it became so.

3. Certain pseudo-scientific conclusions are then developed. They are here quoted from the notes in Scofield's Bible. 'The face of the earth bears everywhere the marks of such a catastrophe.'
'The first creative act . . . gives scope for all the geologic ages.'
'It is by no means necessary to suppose that the life-germ of seeds perished in the catastrophic judgment which overthrew the primitive order. With the restoration of dry land and light the earth would "bring forth" as described. It was the animal life which perished, the traces of which remain as fossils. Relegate fossils to the primitive creation, and no conflict of science with the Genesis cosmogony remains.' (*Scofield Bible*, Notes on Ch. 1).

As, despite the optimism of Scofield's note, it is utterly impossible, if such theory be true, to reconcile the Genesis account with either science or common sense we must needs examine the foundations of this view more closely. Most of the fallacies are quite obvious. In the first postulate the word 'perfect' has been misused. In a succession of creatorial acts each stage is 'perfect' if it achieves the Creator's intention even though the whole thing is not 'perfect', in the final sense, until all the stages are complete.

In verse 1 we have only the beginning and the planet thus created was necessarily unfurnished until the Creator had completed the work outlined in the rest of the chapter. As Isaiah 45. 18 says so clearly, God created the earth in order that it might be inhabited—and by the end of Genesis 1 it was.

The second fallacy lies in the statement that the face of the earth bears everywhere the marks of such a catastrophe. We may well ask 'where?' Which geological formation? Which catastrophe? The geological 'marks on the face of the earth' cover the vast era

---

[1] Granville Penn, writing in 1822, *Mineral and Mosaic Geologies* criticises both Bishop Patrick and the German theologian Rosenmuller for believing in a long period of time between verses 1 and 2 although Rosenmuller rejects the idea of chaos.

from before the Cambrian to the Recent. If the great uplifted masses of basalt of Staffa are evidence of this alleged catastrophe then plainly the twisted shales of Wales or the riven chasm of Cheddar cannot be, for they are separated from one another by whole epochs and by millions of years. The implication of Scofield's note is that the great mountain folds and chasms with rushing streams and beautiful waterfalls are all the work of the evil one who fell and wrecked God's perfect—and presumably flat and mountainless—earth. Or else at best that all these mighty works are the results of God's judgment on some mythical earlier inhabitants of this globe. What lamentable ignorance of the creatorial power of God! It was God who laid the foundations of the mountains and hills—not the Devil! Granite and shale, marble and chalk, mountains and valleys—all have a part in the scheme which the Creator pronounced 'very good'.

The third fallacy lies in the statement that 'the first creative act gives scope for all the geologic ages'. Yet these same geological formations with all their fossils have just been used by Scofield as evidences of catastrophe, i.e. of destruction and not of creation! It is far more usual for holders of the 'Gap hypothesis' to put all the geological ages in the 'gap', and this is plainly what Scofield really means to do.

The contention that the verb in verse 2 means 'to become' waste and void rather than that it 'was' so has been examined by scholars, and the judgment of the best Hebraists[1] is that the text is most naturally translated by 'was'.

The fourth fallacy lies in the quite incredible statement about the life-germs of plants surviving the catastrophe, only the animal life perishing. The statement almost implies that only animal fossils exist but doubtless this is due to the lack of clarity in expression rather than to the editor's lack of knowledge. But even the idea of the life-germs of plants surviving during the ages when animal fossils were forming is astounding. On any scale whatever the geological ages must be measured in thousands— hundreds of thousands—of years. Radio active measurements demand millions of years back to the Cambrian. When did this

---

[1] See e.g. F. F. Bruce, *J. Trans. Victoria Institute*, Vol. LXXVIII, read pp. 21-24, 34-37, 1946. The alternative view is maintained in the same volume by Mr. Heward whose article contains a number of statements which are only partly true, interspersed with much padding and special pleading.

alleged catastrophe take place—before the Cambrian—during the coal age—the age of the great reptiles—which? If they all belong to the 'gap' we have germ-seeds of plants surviving 500 million years!

Finally if it be argued that for a planet to be waste and void —uninhabited and at the moment uninhabitable—is evidence of the work of the Devil then we must confess that the present state of Mars and Venus and indeed of the other planets is evidence of the work of the Devil!

The 'Gap Theory' is then unscriptural, unscientific and unreasonable, and rejecting it completely we can return to the simple study of verse 2.

The state of the earth in the remote past is described by the two words *tohu* and *bohu* and by the statement that darkness surrounded it. The first term seems to mean either empty, formless or possibly invisible. Although the conception 'formless' seems the most probable meaning of the Hebrew, the translation 'invisible' is supported by the Septuagint *aoratos* (not seen) and (though probably not independently) by Josephus and a number of early Christian writers; it would also agree with the concluding statement of the verse regarding the darkness which covered the entire planet.

Probably however the two words taken together imply 'formless and empty'. The remainder of the chapter regards the Creator as giving form—like the Potter—to the world, and filling it with life. That being so His first task must be to bring light into the scene and the conclusion of the verse reminds us of the necessity for this. The earth was covered with water and this uninterrupted ocean was itself wrapped in darkness.

Plainly we have already passed over ages since the initial formation—by whatever means—of the planet. The bulk of the world's water is present as liquid covered with misty vapours. What caused the darkness we do not know. A little ozone in our atmosphere cuts down the ultra violet light, and mist and dust can cut out the entire visible range of light.

The Deep[1] whose face was dark requires more attention for

---

[1] The 'deep'. The great ocean trenches exceed 10,000 metres in depth. At the bottom of these the pressure is of the order of 1000 atmospheres or 7 tons per sq. in. The total volume of the oceans has been estimated at 1.38×10^{18} cubic metres which would weigh 1.38×10^{18} metric tonnes i.e. approx. 1,300,000 million million tons.

it leads to many scientific marvels. Let us content ourselves with just two put in the form of simple questions. What is it made of? Where did it come from? Any school child will answer the first question with great enthusiasm. Water is just H_2O which our young informant will explain for us as 'two parts hydrogen to one of oxygen'. So far, so good. It is quite true that each atom of oxygen has two neighbouring hydrogen atoms to which it is fairly securely linked, but the strange properties possessed by water do not at all agree with what can be predicted for a substance of simple formula H_2O. Such a substance ought to be a gas requiring special liquefaction plant to reduce it to a liquid. Why then is ordinary water a liquid? Because it is not adequately represented by the simple formula H_2O. The Creator who linked all the Bible together by the little Hebrew hook *vaw* has linked all the molecules of water together by a force, only discovered in our own life times, called the 'hydrogen bond'. It is this force which makes water so different from what it would have been. Water is the only inorganic liquid occurring naturally. It is inorganic yet essential in all organic living material. There is no known substitute for water in life, such liquids as wine, milk, juices, etc., being in any case mainly water. Its peculiar property of freezing from the top downwards and its great capacity for heat make it ideal for its tasks on our planet. Only the shallowest seas will freeze solid. The great Gulf Stream makes Britain what it is.[1] Its ability to dissolve oxygen from the air keeps the fishes alive. The God who designed life, designed water for it and supplied the earth with a vast store of it.

This at once brings us to the second question: where did it come from? The outer zones of the earth contain immense quantities of oxygen. Most of this has combined with metals like iron or aluminium or with non-metals like silicon, but back in the early stages of our planet's history much must have combined with the earth's hydrogen before we lost most of this light material. From then on the history of this water-vapour is difficult to follow. Certainly we did not lose it as the other planets have very largely done. For one thing the earth's atmosphere acts as a shield to save water from the steady destruction that it would

---

[1] With its great specific heat, water becomes an ideal heat carrier and hence regulator of temperature. See, for example, Rachel Carson, *The Sea Around Us* Ch. 12. The global thermostat.

suffer by the sun's ultra-violet light. But there is more than a suspicion that for a time much of the earth's water was actually 'dissolved' in molten rocks only to be disgorged again much later as the rocks cooled, and to appear as a vast steamy ocean covering the earth's surface with a great deep and with impenetrable mists. This seems to be the meaning of the words of God in Job 38. 8 'Or who shut up the sea with doors, when it brake forth, as if it had issued out of the womb; when I made the cloud the garment thereof and thick darkness a swaddling band for it?' God goes on to speak of the rise of the continents confining the ocean to its appointed bed, a fact that we shall deal with later. For the present we can only marvel at the accuracy of the metaphor. The oceans were born from the earth, they issued from its womb. Thus the Bible contradicts all ancient mythology which derives the earth from the ocean. The Bible alone of ancient literature knew that the oceans came from the earth.

There is one more wonder yet before we leave this question of the ocean. Not only must water have most unusual properties but there must be enough of it. The amount possessed by Mars would be useless for human life. Astronomers have tried to calculate the amount of water likely to be found on such a planet as ours. Ours is a somewhat unusual planet. We have over 300 times as much oxygen but 10 million times as much water as, with our present knowledge, might have been expected!

This, despite our dislike of rainy days, is not too much.[1] It is all necessary to supply the moisture to provide the rain to give life to the countless millions of creatures that live on the 'dry land'.

Both in quality and quantity the great deep of Genesis 1. 2 is one of the wonders of creation. Those who, failing to look to the purpose beyond, see in the great deep only chaos and destruction, fail to discern the wonderful stages of Creation Planned and Creation Accomplished.

The scene was thus being prepared for the coming of life, but the conditions of temperature and humidity were not yet suitable. The life-giving Spirit could not commence His operation of

---

[1] 'There are 31 million cubic miles of sea water, covering over 70% of the surface of the earth . . . acre for acre it is probably more productive than the land'.—Creatable Resources, F. N. Woodward, B.Sc., Ph.D., in *Journal of Institute of Chemistry.*

bringing life to creatures. He must wait, 'moving' upon the face of the great deep. This moving or hovering is a metaphor borrowed from the eagle fluttering over its nest as can be seen by the use of the same rare word in Deuteronomy 32. 11

> As an eagle that stirreth up her nest
> That *fluttereth* over her young
> He spread abroad His wings.

Thus the Spirit hovered over this little planet until the time came for life to develop. 'Thou sendest forth Thy Spirit', says the Psalmist (Ps. 104. 30)—'they are created'.

To us it may seem strange that an all-powerful Creator should choose to wait—should choose to take ages to form an earth suitable for life—but it is our conception of time that is at fault. Time has a very different meaning to Him. To Him it was but the beginning of a week's work!

And to us it seems that it was a very long time—the whole Old Testament age—before that same Spirit commenced His second and greater task when He hovered, first over a maiden in Galilee, then over a Divine Person at the Jordan and finally over a Church at Pentecost. But to all those born of that Spirit He has given life that is life indeed; into their lives there has shone a Light that is very good; they have experienced a morning to which there is no evening.

CHAPTER 10

LIGHT

And God said, Let there be light:
and there was light.
And God saw the light,
that it was good:
And God divided the light from the darkness.
And God called the light day,
And He called the darkness night,
And there was evening
And there was morning.
The first day.   Gen. 1. 3

THE verses now before us set out in very simple fashion two important truths. First, it is to God alone that we must attribute the coming of light to this planet, and thus surely in the ultimate analysis, the very existence of light itself. Secondly, that the Creator ordained day and night before the coming of life and even before the formation of the continents.

The whole section is very simple and is plainly anthropomorphic. It could not be otherwise, for under no other suitable figure of speech could God explain to us how He produced light or how He made the earth rotate. But we must remember that the figure is maintained consistently throughout and it must not be arbitrarily rejected at certain points. If God chooses to describe His creatorial work under the figure of a man speaking and seeing and doing His work in a six-day week we must accept that He maintains that method of description throughout the chapter and that each phrase is a tiny human picture of something which is far vaster and more difficult to understand.

The first section, then, deals with the coming of light to this planet. God is the creator of light. The whole chapter seems to consist of sections each of which is complete in itself, and each of which concentrates on one major aspect of the subject. Here the account concentrates on the existence of light itself apart from any material cause. Light was made by God; it was good; it brought day to the earth. The sun, moon, and stars will be dealt with quite separately in a later section.

The remainder of the Bible is absolutely consistent with this simple picture. While it recognises many times that this earth derives its light from the sun, it also affirms that light does exist as such—even without any sun. In Psalm 104. 2 God is described as covering Himself with light as with a garment. In Isaiah 45. 7 God declares 'I form *yatsar* (the light) and create *bara*' (darkness,) and in Isaiah 60. 19 the promise is given that 'The sun shall be no more thy light by day . . . for the Lord shall be unto thee an everlasting light'. Saul, on the Damascus road, saw a light that was brighter than the sun.

Thus while from a purely scientific standpoint there can be no doubt that the light which God used in Genesis 1. 3 to bring day and night to this earth was, in fact, the sun's light, that is not the point developed here. In these verses we confine our attention to light as such and to its effects in bringing day and night. There is nothing unscientific about this. A modern text-book is quite likely to discuss light in the abstract long before producing chapters on the sun and moon. It must be remembered that the main purpose of the whole Bible is spiritual and moral and that throughout the remainder of the book light is taken as symbolic of all that God is and does, for 'God is light and in Him is no darkness at all' (1 John 1. 5). It is, then, not to be wondered at that in Genesis 1. 3 God is pleased to deal with light as of prime importance in its own right.

We do not, in the ultimate sense, know what light is. It is part of the basis of the Universe and like energy or matter lies beyond our final analysis. The Bible on the one hand contents itself with telling us that God made light and that it was good. Scientists on the other hand give us some account of how it is made and why it is good. It is made by machines millions of times smaller than the tiniest watch. These machines are called atoms, and within each there are still tinier 'parts' known as electrons which perform incredible dances up and down what are called 'energy levels'. Each time one of these electrons descends from a higher energy level to a lower one it gives out a flash of light whose 'wave length' is strictly governed by a universal law. Scientists measure the energy levels and the wave lengths and marvel at the atoms and molecules that produce such phenomena. The Christian joins them in equal wonder and proceeds still further to reverence for the Master Mind that designed such atoms. The more in future years we are able to learn about electrons and the production of light the greater surely will be our reverence for the Creator.

When an electron falls from a higher energy level to a lower it gives out a flash of light. In a vacuum that flash will travel at 186,000 miles per second for thousands of years. The light which we see from the nebula in Andromeda started from some electron jumps which happened three quarters of a million years ago! But what 'travels'? A flash of light—yes—but what is it?

Some folk, like Sir Isaac Newton, thought that each flash was a tiny particle. A beam of light would be composed of millions of these tiny specks. Others, like Fresnel and Clerk Maxwell, argued that there were no specks, only waves or vibrations. The human mind however demanded that there should be something to vibrate or wave. Scientists even resorted to the invention of an imaginary ether to account for the waves; its properties however were so strange that in the end the idea was abandoned, and we are now left with two possible pictures of light, the corpuscular which regards light as made of tiny particles and the wave theory which treats light as a non-material and purely wave-like phenomenon. Nor is this the end of the story, for even the very electrons themselves that started the ray are treated sometimes as particles and sometimes as waves. It now seems certain that we can in fact hold both views so long as we do not try to apply arguments derived from one aspect to problems raised by the other.

It is this fact that the scientist is convinced that two apparently irreconcilable explanations of a phenomenon may both be true, that has led thoughtful folk to beware of the old fallacy of concluding that a 'religious' or moral explanation of the world is necessarily wrong because its terms cannot be equated with those derived from a scientific study of the same world. A scientific description of what we believe to have been the early history of the earth (at present a very incomplete story) is no more true than the wonderfully simple account of Genesis 1. The two are complementary. The metallurgist who describes a half-crown as a metallic object made of 75% copper and 25% nickel, bearing certain inscriptions impressed on it by metal dies at the mint, is no more correct than the poor widow who describes it as a

'God-send' when she receives it from the Church funds just in time to get a little much-needed extra food. Everything depends upon one's approach to the problem. Light, then, may be regarded as a stream of particles; it may be regarded as a set of waves; it may be regarded as part of the work of God. The three views are complementary.

We must now, however, literally come down to earth, for the verses before us imply that God brought light to this planet; that it was good, i.e. suited to the task He had in view: that He divided the light from the darkness and that He named the two periods of the day.

We have already expressed the opinion that this light came from the sun although that is not the point at issue here. Light and darkness lead in the next verse to morning and evening, to sunrising and sunsetting, so that unquestionably the sun was there. Some think that in those early stages of the world its light was obscured by some covering shroud, whether of mist or gases or dust we do not know. We cannot even be sure when light first came to this planet. Some of the trilobites of the Cambrian age 500 million years ago, had eyes, yet it is obvious that, as Genesis 1 asserts, light came to our planet long before life existed here.

God saw the light that it was good. Why did God bring light to this planet? The building up of organic material is a very complicated process. This difficult task requires not only a considerable amount of energy but energy of exactly the right intensity and in the right amounts. It would seem that, as verses 14 to 18 tell us, the Creator achieved this by designing the solar system in such a way that our planet was at a carefully regulated distance from the sun—so that the light it received should be exactly suited to the growth of green plants and cellulose and to the development of sugars and starches and foodstuffs. Yet it was perfectly fitted also to provide for the synthesis of the beautiful colours in flowers and to maintain the life of the animal creation.

Light travels at a very great speed and thus God is able to use it as a swift messenger to warn us of danger, especially as He has provided us, not only with eyes to register the incoming light with incredible rapidity but also with automatic (reflex) reactions which make us take avoiding action in much less time than the brain could work out the correct response. Light is therefore the greatest single factor in preserving us from danger.

Light also brings us an immense amount of information. Once we have learnt in our early days to interpret what we see, light brings us a wealth of information direct. This is so true, that when we say 'I see' we frequently mean 'I understand' as if seeing a thing was knowing all about it. Light is the greatest single means of conveying information in the universe. When blind folk obtain their sight it takes them some time to learn to interpret what they see. Perhaps we are always learning, or should be, to interpret more fully what we see. There is no doubt that when a person becomes a Christian he interprets what he sees in a new way. Light brings fresh messages to him.

> Heaven above is softer blue,
>   Earth around is sweeter green;
> Something lives in every hue
>   Christless eyes have never seen:
> Birds with gladder songs o'erflow,
> Flowers with deeper beauties shine,
> Since I know, as now I know,
>   I am His and He is mine.

Light brings us into intimate touch with reality. As its rays reveal to us the glory of some beautiful scene it seems to be coming from God Himself. And maybe it is, for what else is beauty but a revelation of some aspect of God?

Light, then, forewarns us of danger, it provides the world with energy, it reveals much of the wonder of the handiwork of the Creator and so operates as to provide in the natural world a wonderful parable that can be used in the spiritual. Surely, light is good.

God has divided the light from the darkness. In other words He so constituted our little planet that it rotates. Why and how it rotates He does not tell us. It is an intriguing problem why everything in the universe seems to revolve or rotate. Astronomers for long attempted to find the origin of this 'angular momentum'. It extends right down to the level of electrons and probably to the tiny particles which exist inside the atomic nucleus itself. It is a fundamental tendency in all 'matter' and its *origin* must lie beyond the limits of our conception and must be assumed to be part of the work of the original creation of the atoms themselves.[1]

---

[1] There is within matter a force, like gravitation yet different, such that when two bodies approach each other they compel each other to revolve about a common centre.

The earth rotates and thus its ordinary inhabitants are carried alternatively through the hours of light and darkness. Why did God do this? On the physical plane we are so built that we must rest at regular intervals and night helps to compel this. But God could have made us otherwise; we are promised a future city where there will be no night; why then did He make night and day? Is not the answer already becoming clear to the reader? Surely already in the Genesis story, in the progress from disorder to order, from emptiness to fulness, from darkness to light we have the plainest indications that God made the material world to fit in with the spiritual. The material world is designed to produce parallels—parables—of the spiritual. There is indeed a spiritual law operating in the natural world, and God put us on a planet where light is separated from darkness for our spiritual education as well as for our physical needs. There is a spiritual as well as a physical reason for the pattern of creation and he who divorces science from true religion will never begin to come to a real understanding of the world.

God called the light day and the darkness night. This is the beginning of true science. When a scientist finds a new set of facts or substances he first separates them into groups and then names them. So God separates light from darkness, clouds from oceans, dry land from sea, and then gives to each class its name. In the next chapter man himself carries on the task of naming the creatures, and this work he has continued to do right down to our own day, there being no apparent end to the task of naming creatures and substances and phenomena.

We come now to the words which have for so long posed a problem:

> There was evening
> There was morning,
> The first day.

How are we to interpret these words, repeated throughout the story for six days until we reach a seventh which has no recorded evening or morning?

The words are no afterthought, no interpolation, no later addition to foster belief in a sabbath. They belong to the structure of the chapter and they fit into the form of the chapter—the Creator describing His work in human terms, yet terms which, as we have seen, have a far vaster meaning than the mere surface value of the human words.[1]

What conception then do these words convey? Surely the first lesson is that the Creator did not choose to bring everything into existence by one single instantaneous act. The work was done in progressive, orderly stages. This is important. We have already mentioned it when considering the word *bara'* and it disposes of the ideas that when God does something it must be what we call instantaneous. God is not limited by our ideas of time. He who created the atomic nucleus in the study of which times like a million million millionth of a second are involved, also created the great galaxies whose histories are measured in thousands of millions of years.[2] When we grasp such facts of science we realise at once that the actual periods of time in creation are, if we may reverently say so, of small importance to the Eternal God.

By describing the work of preparing the world as but a week's work the chapter gives two impressions: (1) that the task was, to God, relatively simple and (2) that relatively it was a short time. Popular science books often try to picture the story of the earth's development by some simple illustration or time chart. The frontispiece of the book shows us stellar time as a twelve-hour clock; the history of the galaxy occupies most of the hours, the time since the fossils first appeared takes up part of the last hour and man's history occupies a few minutes. The scientist is merely doing what God did in Genesis 1—using a simple illustration to convey a correct impression.

The scientist will agree that against the background of the creation of a galaxy of 100,000 million suns involving thousands of millions of years, the task of preparing this one little planet could best be illustrated as a week's work.

And doubtless too there is another lesson. The material task was small compared with the spiritual with which all the rest of the Bible is concerned and which involved at last the Incarnation and the Cross.

The picture, then, of Creation's 'week' is simple and, against a background of galactic time, accurate. It leaves two other

---

[1] 'Of what fashion those days were, it is either exceeding hard or altogether impossible to think'.—Augustine, *The City of God*, Book II. Ch. 6.
[2] Each aspect of reality has its own time scale—galactic, solar, human, insect, atomic, sub-atomic. God in Genesis is picturing solar events in a human time scale.

questions to be investigated. Are the six days meant to be consecutive? Why 'evenings and mornings'?

I do not think the six days are primarily meant to be consecutive although in effect the outline comes very near to that. The chapter deals primarily with six great topics which finally lead up to the coming of man and the completion of God's work. The time involved by those topics may overlap to some extent but each brings the completion of the story one stage nearer. The first three topics are: (1) light (2) air and oceans (3) continents and plant life. This order is essentially logical and scientific and there is no reason to doubt that it is also chronological. The second group of three topics goes back to the same order and carries the work forward. It deals with (4) Times and seasons as regulated by the sun and moon (5) fishes and birds (6) animals and man. No one expects that a modern scientific text book which devotes a succession of chapters to six major topics will at the same time strive to ensure that each chapter begins chronologically where its predecessor ends. Quite frequently the new chapter opens with some such words as 'It will now be necessary to return for a while to some statements which were made earlier in the book . . .' and then the writer brings his new theme forward and finally advances the over-all picture. There is little doubt that this frequently happens in the Bible; the first chapter of Chronicles does not follow chronologically after the last chapter of 2 Kings, it goes back again to the beginning. To some extent even the second chapter of Genesis goes back over the events of Chapter 1. It is, then, quite reasonable to believe that Day 4 goes back chronologically to the beginning again by dealing with a sun and moon which had been created in a remote past and had, in fact, regulated days and seasons for many geological ages. What we are told is that this is part of a unified plan which culminated in the production and completion of a planet suitable for man.

It is more important, then, to stress the topical nature of the six sections rather than to strain the metaphor of the days too far in demanding chronological succession for all six.[1] Yet even so it is certainly amazing that so ancient a document should set out

---

[1] See also Dr. B. Ramm, *The Christian View of Science and Scripture*, p. 144, London 1955 and for an exposition of the theory that days of Genesis 1 are the days on which God revealed to man the account of Creation see Air Commodore P. J. Wiseman, *Creation Revealed in Six Days*, London 1948.

an overall order which commences with an astronomical introduction followed by a geological development leading to the
progressive introduction of vegetable life, fishes, birds, animals
and man. No scientist could ask for more in so brief an account
of creation.

But why 'evenings and mornings'? Some have argued that it
is because Eastern folk commence their days at sunset. Admittedly
the Hebrews do—but why? The day must commence at some time
clearly visible to human beings . . . that is sunrise or sunset. The
'day' in the sense of the bright part plainly commences at sunrise,
but the 'day' in the sense of a complete rotation of the earth must
include a night. The question then arises 'which night belongs
to the day . . . the preceding night or the following night?' Western
folk solved the problem by cutting the night in two and giving
half to yesterday and half to today, but this did not appeal to
many of the peoples of the east. The Hebrews had to make their
choice and they decided that the previous evening and night
belonged to the day. Doubtless they did this because their remote
ancestors did it. If we ask why they in their turn did it, surely
the answer lies back in the earliest teachings current among them,
namely that darkness was there before light . . . evening came
before morning. Yet even so the words used are unexpected.
Evening means sunset or twilight; morning dawn or sunrise. The
tabernacle lamp was lit from evening to morning—for the twelve
hours of darkness—not for the twenty-four hours of a day. It is
difficult to insist that the terms 'evening and morning' mean
twenty-four hours. Some have translated the passage as 'evening
came and then morning came' and this is good so long as we do
not seek to reckon the morning as belonging to the next day.
Perhaps it is best to keep to the stark simplicity of the Revised
Version—'there was evening and there was morning, one day' . . .
or 'the first day'. Admitting, then, that there is some difficulty
in deciding why the words evening and morning were chosen,
let us ask what inferences can be drawn from this phrase.

Firstly, if evening is sunset and morning sunrise, the sun must
already have been created and the earth must have been revolving
around it and rotating on its own axis. Verse 14 cannot then be
taken to mean that the sun was created later than the coming of
light to the earth.

Secondly the words, even though pictorial, imply that time has some meaning—time is measurable. This may seem either very obvious or very philosophical but there have been some who suggest that time had no meaning—i.e. in a sense was not created —before the coming of man.

But the third inference seems to me of far greater importance than the other two. The six-fold repetition of the order, evening— morning, is God's way of emphasizing that each stage of His work was progressing from disorder to order, from darkness to light. It lays a foundation on which all of the rest is built. God will never finish His work in the dark. God is working His purpose out through successive ages, through times of gloom as well as of enlightenment, through the evenings of man's doubt and sorrow and sin, through the evening of the Crucifixion to the early morning of the Resurrection and the sunrise of a glorious Return beyond which, as on the seventh day, there is no recorded evening.

When God's work is finished it will be morning.

CHAPTER 11

THE FIRMAMENT

And God said,
    Let there be a firmament in the midst of the waters,
and let it divide the waters from the waters.
And God made the firmament,
    and divided the waters which were under the firmament
        from the waters which were above the firmament:
            and it was so.
And God called the firmament Heaven.
    And there was evening
    and there was morning,
    a second day.   Gen. 1. 6-8 R.V.

THE second section of the creation story deals with the earth's atmosphere. It is at once noticeable that the Creator is continuing the work of dividing and separating. A perfectly uniform universe would be meaningless . . . to use a scientific term it would have reached its maximum entropy and presumably nothing further could happen. But the universe is not uniform and the Creator has divided and separated many things . . . in the section before us He separates the clouds from the oceans. This He does by means of what we call the atmosphere and what the Bible calls a firmament or expanse.

The original idea behind the Hebrew word *raqia'* (firmament) seems to be the process of beating or stamping out. In the development of language this has led to two distinct meanings. If clay in a mould is stamped on it will become compressed—firmer—more solid. Hence in later times some have supposed that the Hebrews conceived of a solid roof over the sky, a dome to which the stars were affixed. This misconception is partly due to the Septuagint translation of the word in question by the Greek word *stereoma* which is nearer in meaning to solid than to space or expanse. But the word *raqia'* was connected with a second and much commoner conception. If gold or silver was beaten or stamped out it became very thin. The ancients were in fact very good at this process and specimens of their work show that they used gold leaf down to $\frac{1}{5000}$th of an inch thick. The word thus acquired the meanings of expanse and of thinness and we find this borne out in related expressions such as the word *raq* used for Pharaoh's 'thin' kine and *raqiq* used for 'wafers'. One of the clearest uses of the verb is in 2 Samuel 22. 43 where we read, 'Then I did beat them as small as the dust of the earth. I did *stamp* them as the mire of the street and did spread them abroad'. We note that stamping leads to spreading out or expansion. In Isaiah 42. 5 and 44. 24 the word is used as a complement to the word for 'stretching out' . . . 'He stretcheth out the heaven and spreadeth out the earth'. In Exodus 39. 3 the verb is used again for beating out the gold into thin sheets so that it could later be cut into threads. The force of the word in Genesis 1 is clearly, then, that of an expanse, something very thin, which separated the clouds from the oceans. God called this firmament or expanse 'heaven', a word which, as we have already seen, by its very form denotes 'that which is extended'. Finally, just as the word heaven is sometimes used in a narrower, sometimes in a wider, sense, so the word firmament is used not only of the earth's atmosphere but, as in verses 14-17, of interstellar space. The word once again is carefully chosen for just as gold can be stamped out (*raqa'*) so wonderfully thin that the finest gold leaf is less than 500 atoms thick, so the firmament (*raqia'*) becomes so fine that, in outer space, its density drops to 10^{-19}, i.e. 1/10000000000000000000 that of water.

The origin of the earth's atmosphere seems to be somewhat obscure. We have, as already mentioned, about three hundred times as much oxygen as would have been expected and perhaps over a hundred thousand times as much nitrogen. As in the case of water it seems possible that these gases were once dissolved in the molten rocks of the earth. Another curiosity of our atmosphere —namely the existence of nearly 1% of argon—and the fact that that argon is unexpectedly heavy, has been explained as being due to the gradual radioactive transformation of the heavier potassium atoms of the earth into argon. If this process has followed the usual law of radioactive transformation it must have taken hundreds of millions of years.

Our atmosphere is unique in the solar system. No other planet has an atmosphere that could possibly support human life though doubtless the Creator could form creatures capable of existing in atmospheres of methane or ammonia![1] But we are not so fitted. We are exactly fitted for the atmosphere which God has made for us and a thoughtful contemplation of this atmosphere must convince all but the hardened materialist that the 'firmament' of Genesis 1 was planned by an Omniscient Creator.

All living things depend ultimately for their substance on carbon dioxide and water. The air provides both of these, the carbon dioxide in its actual make-up and the water which it carries as vapour and deposits as rain or mist. Air of course contains, above all else, the life-giving, health-controlling oxygen, while God has designed us to utilize this by means of a remarkable fluid, blood, which takes up the essential oxygen and distributes it around the body with much greater ease and efficiency than the Gas Board distributes gas around a town. The atmosphere also contains vast quantities of nitrogen which not only dilutes the oxygen to the right level for us, but provides—by devious and wonderful routes—the nitrates and other nitrogen compounds required as 'fertilizers' in the soil. The composition of this wonderful atmosphere is kept near enough to constant by the stirring action of the winds, by the solubility to some extent of the gases in the oceans and by complicated cyclic processes among living things and rocks.

Besides all this the atmosphere provides us with a shield from the various rays of the sun. These include not only 'heat' rays and what we call light, but powerful ultra-violet beams which would probably kill us in a matter of minutes if we were not screened by the oxygen which—in the upper atmosphere—gives a tiny but highly efficient protective barrier sufficient to save our lives. The air also shields us from other effects of incoming rays.[2]

Yet further, the atmosphere is the carrier of water vapour without which we should have no rain. It is partly the carrier of pollen and seeds and hence essential to the development of plant life.

---

[1] The larger planets have atmospheres consisting of such gases as hydrogen, ammonia and methane. The atmosphere of Venus seems to be largely carbon dioxide. Prof. R. G. Norrish, Proc. Chem. Soc., Sept. 1958. p. 247.

See also *Atmospheric Photochemistry* Sir Harrie Massey and Dr. A. E. Potter, *Royal Institute of Chemistry, Lecture Series* 1961. No. 1.

[2] 'The sun's rays provide sufficient energy and of the right wave length to have destroyed the entire oceans of the world in 1000 million years.'—R. C. W. Norrish (Cambridge), *Some isothermal reactions of free radicals studied by kinetic spectroscopy.* Proc. Chem. Soc., Sept. 1958, p. 247.

The atmosphere provides us with a warm shelter or blanket without which the earth's temperature would sink so low as to plunge us into a universal ice age. Yet again the atmosphere is responsible for the existence of twilight and in fact without it we should see an intensely hot and brilliant sun in an almost black sky. Thus we might continue, for the atmosphere enables birds and many insects to fly, and permits sounds to travel—noises to warn us and music to cheer us—and cushions us against the constant bombardment of meteorites from outer space!

To the casual reader it might have seemed excessive to devote one whole section out of six to the earth's atmosphere. Yet scientifically once again this is seen to be absolutely justified and the simple story of Genesis 1 vindicated.

CHAPTER 12

THE THIRD DAY—VEGETATION

And God said,
  Let the waters under the heaven be gathered together unto
one place, and let the dry land appear:
                        and it was so.
And God called the dry land Earth;
       and the gathering together of the waters
       called He Seas.
And God saw that it was good.
And God said,
  Let the earth put forth grass,
            the herb yielding seed,
           and the fruit tree yielding fruit
               after his kind,
                  whose seed is in itself,
         upon the earth:
And the earth brought forth grass,
           the herb yielding seed after his kind,
           and the tree yielding fruit,
               whose seed was in itself,
               after his kind:
And God saw that it was good.
    And there was evening
    And there was morning,
    A third day.   Gen. 1. 9-13

THE earth was intended as the home for man and man was
intended and designed for dry land. We should, therefore, expect
the Creator's account of His work to tell us something about the
continents on which we live, and this is done in two delightfully
simple sentences. At the Creator's command the waters were
gathered into one place and dry land appeared.

Yet how careful and accurate the phrasing. If the account had
suggested that the dry land had gathered in one place—one
vast continent—how inaccurate it would have been. It is the
water which makes one continuous stretch and yet the author
does not call it 'Sea' but 'Seas', for as a study of a map or globe

reveals, the great expanses of water, though really one, can best be regarded as divided into great seas. The second sentence— Let the dry land appear . . . is equally remarkable. It tells plainly that the continents were once submerged beneath the oceans. No early Hebrew writer could have had sufficient knowledge of the continents to know that this simple sentence is scientifically true . . . but it is.

The rise of the continents is a vast and intriguing problem. These great continental masses are made up mainly of rocks like granite with a specific gravity of about 2.7, i.e. about 170 lbs. to the cubic foot. They rest upon, or rather in, denser rocks made of aluminium silicate and magnesium silicate. In fact they might almost be said to float in the underlying layers somewhat as an iceberg floats in water. Indeed it is possible that when the underlying zones were hotter the continental masses sank lower and when the earth cooled they rose—or appeared. Professor Joly has even tried to calculate the chances that radio-activity will yet again melt the lower basaltic layers causing the continents to sink once more, with disastrous consequences to the beings who live upon them. But leaving aside Professor Joly's theory, which so far lacks sufficient evidence to make it convincing, we must nevertheless marvel both at the work of the Creator in producing the continents and in the accuracy of the several very simple references to this work.

The dry land has veritably 'appeared' and the waters have 'gone down by the valleys to the place which Thou hast founded for them' (Ps. 104. 8) to the place 'where they shall come but no further, where their proud waves are stayed' (Job 38. 11). God, in His masterly challenge to Job in the chapter just referred to, declares, in vivid poetical language, that the foundations of the earth rest like sockets made to sink into supports—just as the tabernacle boards had sockets and 'bases'.[1] So the continental masses do, in fact, have their foundations set down deeply among the heavier rocks, and these in turn rest upon the great massive shell of still heavier rocks—the corner stone to use the picture language of Job 38. 6 on which the whole 'building' rests. How wonderfully all the rocks of the earth's outer and inner layers are balanced we are only just beginning to learn. As we contemplate

---

[1] Whereupon were the foundations (Heb. sockets) fastened (Heb. made to sink) Job 38. 6 (Literal translation).

the vastness of this aspect of the Creator's activity we cannot do better than use the words of Isaiah when he spoke of the God 'who comprehended the dust of the earth in a measure and weighed the mountains in scales and the hills in a balance' (Isa. 40. 12).

It is not sufficient merely to have the right amount of water on the earth. It is also important that there should be a correct proportion between the surface areas of land and sea. Had the oceans been twice as deep and only half the area, the continents would have been much vaster—but very much drier. Huge inland deserts, dwarfing the Sahara and Gobi, would have stretched across vast areas. But, as we have seen from the wonderful poetic pictures of Psalm 104 and Job 38, the Creator set bounds and limits to the oceans. He who weighed the continents in His balances 'measured the oceans in the hollow of His Hand' . . . and His measurements are very exact.

The continents have been below the oceans—parts of them, like our own little islands, many times. Hence the clay, the slate, the coal, the limestone, the chalk . . . Was it all chance—haphazard? Was it the work of fallen angelic beings? Or was it part of the preparation of a marvellous scene in which mankind should at last use these things in the working out of his history?

Finally we may well ask, 'Was it just the operation of blind geological forces with no ultimate controlling and planning Mind that arranged an ocean—the Mediterranean—to run through the centre of the ancient world—to set the stage for Phoenicia and Crete, for Egypt and Greece and Rome? And was it chance, or the design of One who set bounds to the seas, that in geologically recent times a little strip of water should separate our island from the coast of France? But all history, as Philip of Spain, Napoleon and Hitler, to name but three, have realised, was influenced by those twenty-two miles of water.

Man was designed to live on the dry land . . . but not in a desert. Hence, just as we should expect, the Creator tells us next of the clothing of the continents with vegetation. That vegetation has had a very long history, going back at least to what are called Silurian times, but no one knows how much farther back.

It would be quite foreign to the whole scheme of Genesis 1 to expect a detailed discussion of the chronology of palaeobotany or of the processes involved in the development of plant-life. On the purely scientific side the subject bristles with problems.

Fossil land-plants go back in time as far as the rocks of Devon and sea-plants even further. Whether the graphite of pre-Cambrian days, above 500 million years ago, bears witness to an earlier vegetation we must leave it to geologists to discuss. How such highly complex structures as seeds were ever formed must remain a mystery. The incredibly complicated chemical substances which make up a tiny seed have indeed been analysed by the chemist. Most of them could be, and many have been, synthesised in the laboratory. Yet the more research unfolds of the complexity of these syntheses the more obvious does it become that these substances could never have put themselves together by chance . . . the more appallingly foolish becomes the materialists' theory of a primitive ocean filled with wonderful molecules which joined themselves together to make proteins and enzymes—and hey-presto!—plants and animals and man all followed as a purely natural consequence. The Psalmist was certainly right in what he called those who say that there is no God!

In their long history many of these plants seem to have undergone some change. Some have died out. At times new kinds seem to have arisen. This problem, generally considered under the somewhat wide and vague title of 'evolution', merits some consideration. Obviously it will apply to the animal world as well so that it will be best to consider the whole problem at this point.

Three questions arise. Firstly, we should like to know whether one type of plant or animal may, in the course of many generations, become changed into something appreciably different. Secondly, if some such change is possible, have all forms of life descended from one ancestor, or from a small number of ancestors? Thirdly, if some modification is possible by what mechanism might it be produced?

There are certainly many facts. In the study of both ancient plants and bygone animals the number of facts is legion. We can but seek for an overall impression from these facts and ask what certain answer they give to the above questions.

On the first question we can say that both plants and animals can show a considerable range of modifications both at the same time in history and over a succession of eras. Those modifications which we are able to study at a given time, e.g. the dogs or horses or oak trees of the present day, show a range of sizes, shapes, and even colours etc., within a common recognisable pattern. The modifications of dogs, for example, may be so different from each other as to make the crossing of two of them impossible. We feel, however, content to leave them within the species 'dog'. Perhaps it is true that if we go backwards over a long stretch of time we can see an even wider range of modifications of a creature that we could recognize as, say, a horse. It may even be true that many of the different forms or species of beetles that we now know are descended from a smaller number of species of beetles.

But over against the immense number of facts—the vast armies of fossils showing modifications of creatures within a common recognizable pattern or group—is the still more staggering number of gaps. Every time we meet with some completely new pattern of life we are faced with gaps in the fossil record. Admittedly we should expect the record to be incomplete owing to the great geological upheavals that have taken place. But there are far too many gaps for any simple theory of evolution by constant gradual modification alone. Flowering plants are but one example. As one turns the pages of Professor Seward's great work, *Plant Life through the Ages*, one meets such passages as 'The Evolution of the Flowering Plants—an unsolved problem' . . . and 'It is generally agreed that the early Cretaceous angiosperms such as Platanus, Magnolia and other genera which seem to spring from the earth as Melchizedeks of the vegetable kingdom with no apparent lineage, cannot be the oldest representatives of the class'. There may have been—Professor Seward thinks there were—some precursors of this vast wave of new forms of plant life. The overall picture is clear enough. Time and time again some great new form or pattern of life appears suddenly in the fossil record. A few creatures of intermediate type can sometimes be assigned to the gap before them. It seems pitifully inadequate to plead every time that there must be a continuous series of fossils showing every minute step of variation but that we have lost just the very one which would settle the question. While some still cling to the idea that every form has arisen by the steady, random modification of its predecessors, others are facing up to the overwhelming pressure of facts—new forms arise relatively suddenly and often in vast numbers in the fossil record. One quotation will illustrate the view of many:

'There are many jumps. I do not say that there are no bridges but I submit that the advance of nature which brings with it really *new* features is by steps or by leaps and not by sliding over bridges. It is my belief then, that in the broad domain of nature, natural leaps are many . . . so many that I have ventured to speak of the advance of Nature as fundamentally jumpy. This may no doubt be shocking for those who yearn for continuity but one must speak as one finds!'[1]

Scientifically then, we can approach the second question, that of the number of original forms of life, with a very open mind. We might prefer to believe that there was but one form of life which underwent constant modification down the ages. Every now and again this modification became rapid, widespread and productive of new forms so wonderfully fitted for their environment as to render pure chance variation an utterly inadequate cause. But there is nothing among scientific facts to compel us to accept a single ancestor. It would be just as logical, though possibly less attractive to our way of thinking, to argue that since life arose once by some method which we do not know—and produced creatures which incidentally are also quite unknown to us (there is no proof whatever that the amoeba was created first)—then life might have originated at least twice, once in the vegetable realm and once in the animal and might have produced several or even many forms of life, at the same time or at least within the same era.[2]

The third question, namely, by what mechanism could the variation have been produced, can be studied from the point of view of historical theories and actual experimental investigations.

Historically there are two main theories. Lamarck considered that creatures reacted towards their environment in such a way as to suit it better, and having done so, handed on to their offspring some part of this gain in suitability. Thus changing environment was matched by changing offspring and there was always some inherent force operating to keep the creature in line with the environment.

Darwin, however, commenced from the viewpoint that offspring

---

[1] Dr. Conwy Lloyd Morgan, *Evolution in the Light of Modern Knowledge*, p. 108.

[2] Dr. F. O. Bower: 'It is quite gratuitous to assume that all life sprang from a single source. Many doubt whether for the kingdom of plants at least there ever was a single "trunk" or common source for all. Others assert most definitely that there was not.' *Evolution in the Light of Modern Knowledge*, p. 163.

always differ slightly from their parents and among a numerous variable progeny some would suit their environment better than others. In the constant struggle for existence the weaker varieties would perish in greater numbers than the stronger until the existing population consisted mainly of the newer and stronger form. This story would be repeated throughout the eras of time and hence all present forms might have arisen from one ancestor, or at most a few.

On the side of experimental investigation several facts have been substantiated. The first is the amazing power of reproducing true to type possessed by all living things and the incredible difficulty of producing real modifications. The second fact is the remarkable ability of creatures to adapt themselves to a range of variations in their environments, but at the same time the almost complete absence of any evidence that acquired adaptations can be passed on to the offspring.[1] Some do feel that, over very long periods of time, Lamarck's inherited adaptation might have to be reckoned with. Thirdly, following the work of Mendel, there have been careful studies of the tiny 'pattern carriers' in the germ cells —the chromosomes and the still smaller 'genes'. The ways in which these are linked or may be rearranged have been studied and thus the mechanism of ordinary variation has, to some extent, been unravelled. Severe alterations to these minute structures, such as might arise by bombardment with X-rays or other powerful forces, cause considerable change in the creature and the results are called mutations.

The possibility that mutations might be the origin of new species and orders has been considered but on the whole the mutations caused by the random actions of such 'blind' forces as electro-magnetic waves or radioactive particles seem less well fitted for their environment than their predecessors. There may be a few exceptions but if the mutation theory is to succeed in accounting for the relatively rapid introduction into the geological eras of new forms of life so well fitted for their environment, some 'better' forces than X-rays, or cosmic rays will have to be invoked.

Taking, then, an overall picture of the history of living things on this planet we may say that on a number of occasions completely new forms of life have appeared in geologically relatively

---

[1] See 'Industrial Melanism'. Peppered Moths *The New Scientist,* July 3rd 1958, p. 299.

short periods of time. These forms seem to be too remarkably well fitted to survive to be due solely to the operation of natural selection on random variations. The period in which they must have arisen could not have been long enough for so laborious a method. They arise too suddenly: they survive—many of them into modern times. Some other factor must be invoked. The extreme paucity of intermediate steps or forms when we come to really new organs or whole patterns of life compels the belief that the change was relatively rapid, and, so far as the cell structure was concerned, was at a very deep level. Chance mutations seem inadequate: at this stage and level we must admit the operation of some natural law or force which we have not so far recognised.

The Creator, having introduced from time to time new forms of life well suited to their environment by some means not yet understood, also provided them with the possibility of variation —either by random changes as per Darwin, or by some possible long-term slight response to environment as per neo-Lamarckism or by some chemical, catalytic or radiation-influenced changes which might not be really 'random'—or by all of these—a variation which gives the new form a greater chance of keeping in equilibrium with its gradually changing environment.[1]

To the Christian this is *all* God's work. It is utterly wrong to invoke the intervention of a Creator at the stage which we do not happen to understand but to 'do without' Him when we happen to have understood some part of the mechanism by which He worked. God could have made reproduction 'after its kind' to be as absolutely stereotyped as the mass production of buttons or drawing pins. The creatures might have been made to reproduce with the precision of a modern die-casting machine. God's plan of reproduction—true to overall pattern with the possibility of variation—is infinitely superior.

With some such thoughts in our minds let us return to Genesis I to see what it really tells of the origin and development of life.

Firstly, so far as the plant kingdom is concerned, it would seem that there is a very simple classification into two classes—herbs and trees. The classification is not meant to be in line with any modern definition of these. The word for tree simply means a plant with a wooden trunk . . . the word is sometimes used for

---

[1] See chapters on 'Replication' in Penguin *New Biology*.

wood. The passage simply means that God caused the earth to produce all forms of vegetable life from grasses to the largest trees. Neither can the word 'fruit' be compared with a modern scientific definition of fruit. The word is used throughout the Bible in a very wide sense. The Hebrews saw, in fact, that there was no difference in principle in the reproduction of life—plant, animal or human—for we read of the 'seed' of Abraham and of the 'fruit of thy cattle' and of the 'fruit of thy body'. Seeds and fruits were the vehicles of the reproduction of life. Each kind or kin reproduced its own kind or kin.

As to the process by which the Creator caused vegetable life to arise the passage gives little clue. The words may be translated 'Let the earth put forth grass'—or 'sprout sproutage' or 'vegetate vegetation' . . . for the verb and the noun are almost identical. Seeing that the earth is commanded to do this it may be legitimate to deduce that it occurred by the use of natural forces already operating on this planet and to that extent open to scientific investigation. On the other hand the fact that the command of God is also involved may mean that forces not ordinarily at work on this planet were called into play, or more probably that the common forces which we can investigate were divinely controlled at this stage for the production of life.[1] There is certainly no suggestion that plants were made out of nothing; the text clearly teaches that they are produced from pre-existing matter. Beyond these slight clues the Bible does not tell us how God produced plant-life on the earth. Since scientists also have no clue as to how plant-life arose there is obviously no conflict at this point.

Some folk have, however, imagined that there is a conflict between the term 'after its kind' and the evolutionary view that one species might change into several in the course of a long time. On the scientific side we have already seen that life does not reproduce with the exact mechanical precision of a coin-minting machine. If all human beings were identical the world would be a peculiar place. The Creator has allowed for variation, and over long periods of time with wide changes of environment He doubtless has permitted considerable variation. We do not, however, know what have been the real limits, whether they cross the

[1] There is always a relationship between the type of soil in a district and the type of plants which grow there, just as there is always a relationship between the animal life and the plant life in any given locality.

boundary of what we now call families or orders. If we define a species as a collection of creatures which now freely interbreed in the natural condition and which do not breed freely with the members of any other species we must remember that such is only in fact our definition of the modern English word and tells us nothing of what happened in the past. It is probable that the Hebrews meant no more by their word *min*.[1] They observed the obvious fact that each kind of tree reproduced its own kind; each type of animal produced its like. This simple, obvious fact—so Genesis 1 taught them—was part of the work of God. They were not concerned with modern definitions which in any case vary among different authors. Genesis 1 simply asserts a universally recognized truth; it makes no attempt to define 'kind' nor to discuss variations. But it may be asked whether other Bible writers ever define 'kind' for us. The only other passage that helps is Leviticus 11 with the corresponding passage in Deuteronomy 14. Here we read such expressions as 'every raven after its kind' and the 'hawk after its kind'. Now it is not certain what birds are here included in the terms *'oreb* and *nets*; the former seems to include not only the raven but probably the rook and the crow and *nets* includes several types of 'hawks' as the kestrel and the sparrowhawk. The point at issue is that the word 'kind' can hardly be identified with the modern term species. There are two 'species' of raven in the Middle East and the crow and raven belong to quite different 'species' in the modern sense. It therefore appears that either we must translate the phrase as 'every kind of raven' or 'the raven and birds of a similar kind'. But if this is so all attempts to force the Hebrew *min* to equal some modern definition of 'species' breaks down and Genesis 1 is left free from any arbitrary effort to compel it to mean that God created every 'species' (in our modern sense) separately and that these were compelled for all time to breed within those limits. The passage does not discuss variation in the geological ages. It merely stresses that life reproduces its overall pattern through the wonderful agency of 'seeds' or 'fruits'. And when we see how little the oak tree has changed since the cretaceous era—possibly in 100 million years—and when fishermen discover a coelocanth similar to that whose ancestors lived 200 million years ago, it is perhaps

---

[1] Heb. *min*=race, stock, breed, class, family.

worth remarking that the Author of Genesis 1 was stressing an amazing—though very commonplace—fact when He stressed that living things do reproduce after their own 'kind'.

To the Hebrew and to the Christian it is all part of God's work—His planned creation. Whether we think of the amazing regularity of reproduction true to general pattern for millions of years or of the variations which He has plainly allowed for obvious reasons of variety and suitability to His purposes, we can only conclude, as God Himself did when He surveyed everything that He had made (v. 31), that it was *very good*.

CHAPTER 13

THE FOURTH DAY—SUN, MOON AND STARS

And God said,
  Let there be *lights*
      in the firmament of the heaven
      to divide the day from the night;
and let them be
      for signs, and for seasons,
    and for days, and for years:
and let them be
      for lights in the firmament of the heaven
      to give light upon the earth:
and it was so.
And God made the two *great lights*;
      the *greater light*   to rule the day
    and the *lesser light*   to rule the night:
and God set them
      in the firmament of the heaven
      to give light upon the earth,
    and to rule over the day
    and   over the night,
    and to divide the light from the darkness:
and God saw that it was good.
and there was evening
and there was morning,
    a fourth day.   Gen. 1. 14-19

ONE half of the story is now complete. The starry host is set and this little planet has been furnished with an open sky, with deep oceans and with dry land covered with vegetation. The empty stage is set. It requires filling. The story now proceeds to describe that which occupies the heaven—sun, moon and stars, then that which occupies air and ocean—the birds and fishes, and finally that which occupies the dry land—the animals and man.

Thus viewed the sequence is simple and logical yet it must be agreed that Day 4 has been a puzzle to many and especially to those who hold the theory that the days are meant to represent consecutive periods. The difficulty is obvious enough to all—we have apparently light three days before the sun.

The proposed solutions of the problem have been varied. Those who have supported the hypothesis that the days of creation are meant to represent actual 24-hour days have assumed, either that the sun was created before day 1 but that its light was obscured until day 4, or else that the sun was created on the fourth day, the earlier light being some nebulous emanation. On the latter theory the grasses and trees of day 2 had to exist for 24 hours on this nebulous light. The coal measures then either extracted their vast stores of energy from this nebulous light in 24 hours or, according to the gap theory, in the imaginary gap between verses 1 and 2.

Those who have taken the days as eras have been likewise divided. Those who hold the creation of the sun and moon on the fourth day have supposed the original light to have been derived from some other source such as a nebulous cloud. A case might conceivably be made out for the earth's wandering for some very long time bathed in this 'cosmic' light until—in the fourth stage of its development—it was captured by the star we now call our sun. Before this, plant life had appeared and thereafter animal life arose on the earth. Such a theory would have the merit of agreeing with those views of the origin of the solar system which postulate that the earth was formed from cosmic matter and was captured by the sun at a much later stage. But the theory involves too many astronomical improbabilities in suggesting that the delicate balance of plant life on this planet could survive such a mighty change. If such a capture ever took place it was surely long before life appeared on this planet.

Others think that while sun, moon and stars had been created in the beginning, the full light of these had been largely obscured by reason of some dust, vapours or carbon dioxide in the atmosphere throughout the first three stages of the world's development, usually taken to be from the Cambrian to the Carboniferous. In the fourth era this obscuring medium was removed, as might be conceived possible if the coal measures represent carbon removed as dioxide from the air. One difficulty here is the fact that coal does not occur at one single epoch, but has been formed at times actually many millions of years apart. It is also not certain what would be the effect of returning all this carbon to the air as dioxide because the increased pressure of carbon dioxide in the air would be accompanied by an increased solubility in the oceans. Yet another theory has maintained that on the fourth Day the sun was merely appointed[1] to its task—it had been there before. One suggestion is that at this stage God finally adjusted the orbits of the earth and moon and having thus fixed the times and seasons He could rightly speak of appointing them to rule on the fourth day. This may be a possible translation of the text but does not fit the simple, obvious meaning of the section which puts everything connected with the sun and moon together in the account of the fourth day. That there has been a change in the length of the day is almost certain but it has been extremely slow and gradual and most of it must have occurred before the appearance of plants (i.e. day 3).

So far then as our limited knowledge of science, and our cautious but reverent attempts to understand the form of description used in Genesis 1 will permit, we revert to the explanation offered throughout these pages that the inspired pictures deal with six great topics, the second three of which fill out and complete the first three and, so far as time is concerned, each day may look back to some remote past, but at its close brings the story one stage nearer to completion.

God, then, away back in the beginning created the sun and moon, the earth and the stars. We do not know the exact points in time when these events occurred. Scientifically it is doubtful whether it is even right to speak of a date for such events. Theologically such information would be of no value. The Bible seeks to establish one great fact—in contradistinction to the beliefs of Babylon, Assyria, Egypt and numerous other lands— the sun and moon are not gods, they are but part of the handiwork of the one true God. Perhaps that one great fact is expanded into a second, for the passage enforces the view that not only did God create the sun and moon but that He did so with a purpose and as part of a plan. It is left to scientists to study that plan and in amazement—or reverence—to wonder at its perfection.

Some part of the purpose of God in this solar scheme is

---

[1] God made ('asah) two great lights and set (nathan) them . . . cf. Gen. 18. 8 the calf which Abraham had 'dressed' ('asah) was set (nathan) before his visitors. Quoted from article by A. R. G. Chamings in *Bible League Quarterly*, Jan. 1959, p. 73.

revealed to us in the text to which we now turn. The three aspects outlined are:

1. The provision of light, v. 15. 'To give light upon the earth.'
2. The orderly measurement of time, v. 14. . . . for days and for years.
3. The provision of evidence of a Divine control in history v. 14 . . . for signs and for seasons.

'Let them be for lights in the firmament of the heaven' says v. 15, 'to give light upon the earth . . . and it was so'. We have already said something about light in general in Chapter 10 but here we are concerned with two particular types of light, sunlight and moonlight. God gave us just the right kind of sun and just at the right distance away. Sirius or Vega would not have suited us. The light we receive must be exactly suited to all the needs of the living things which the Creator proposed to put on this planet. The plants are provided with the wonderful substance, chlorophyll, which absorbs the energy needed from the reds and blues of sunlight and reflects the intenser green rays, thus preventing the leaves from receiving more energy than they need. The photosynthetic processes in plants are so geared to sunlight that they run at an amazing level of efficiency. But so also are human eyes, which can detect in the range of the sun's spectrum above a hundred different hues, and yet when they are all combined in sunlight sees but one effect which we call white. This greater light, however, must be replaced by a much softer and gentler light at night if man and beasts are to enter into restful sleep. So, for the night, God provided the lesser light with a light-giving power only 1/700,000 that of the sun. Well does the Hebrew choose a word which means 'much less by contrast'.

In addition to its function as the provider of light to the earth, the sun is also commissioned to regulate our days and years (v. 14). These are in fact governed by the relative distances at which the members of the solar system are set. If we ask the simple question, 'Does it matter much how long these days and years are?' we shall see that from a human standpoint the answer is very important and from a scientific and theological standpoint very interesting.

The length of the year is determined by the fact that we are travelling at an average speed of about 18.5 miles per second around an elliptical orbit with a mean distance from the sun of about 93 million miles. If these figures were altered, many things

on earth would alter as well. If our planet was at the distance of
Mars we should be ice-bound. If we lived on Pluto we should
have but one New Year's day every 250 years! That perhaps
would not matter, but if the planet's axis was inclined like the
earth's we should have only one summer and one harvest every
250 years, and that summer on Pluto would not be warm enough
to give any harvest anyway. The length of the year and the distance
of the earth from the sun are not arbitrary functions of a purpose-
less Universe; they fit into a plan. The length of time between
harvests is of supreme importance to the population of the world.
The intensity of the sun's light and the rate of plant growth are
both regulated to give that bountiful supply of food which God
provides and man could enjoy if he distributed it wisely.

The length of the day is also of great importance. It needs
little imagination to consider how very awkward life would be if
we had a day of nine hours like Jupiter's. We should sleep for
three or four hours and work for three or four with the remainder
for meals and miscellaneous tasks. Conversely if our day were, as
the moon's, about a month long, we might have to sleep for ten
days or more—or else work through long stretches of night.
There is little doubt that the human machine is 'built' (i.e.
designed or planned) to function efficiently if it rests through some
six to eight hours of darkness out of every twenty-four hours,
and nothing but the 24-hour day compels man to regulate his
whole life so drastically as that. Man as an individual requires a
24-hour day. The human race as a whole requires a harvest
every 365 days . . . every year. It is true that God has allowed a
good margin of safety and man on occasions can work for forty-
eight or even seventy-two hours at a stretch, and on the larger
scale harvests may fail in a given area for several seasons—but
this in no way affects the overall importance of the 24-hour day
and the 365¼ day year as the ideal for the beings that live here.

But how did God use the sun and moon to control these
periods? The length of the year is governed by the velocity of
the earth and the force of gravity between earth and sun. The
origin of the earth's velocity in its orbit is at present unknown
although there are some theories to account for it, but given
that velocity the length of the year becomes fixed by the fact
that the outward centrifugal force of the earth is balanced by
the inward gravitational attraction of the sun. Thus the sun is

'for years'. The exact cause for the day being twenty-four hours is also unknown. Some think that the earth at one time rotated more quickly. Certainly the rising and falling of the tides is tending to slow the earth down by a kind of brake-like drag. Yet it seems that sun and moon raise not only ocean tides but small solid 'tides' by slight deformation of the solid earth, and also quite definite atmospheric tides whose 'high tide' comes some 2 hours before midday and midnight. The calculation of the effect of these three tides is a fantastically complicated problem but it is probable that the net effect is to bring the earth to its present constant rotation giving a 24-hour day. The sun and moon do then control the day. Thus from a human standpoint the length of the day and the year are all important, from the scientific standpoint they are extremely interesting, and from the theological standpoint are evidences of a unity of plan from astronomical down to human levels.

The greater and the lesser lights were also given for 'signs' and for 'seasons'. Some lexicons consider that the second term refers to the natural seasons and ancient calendars frequently name the months by some such scheme as 'the month of barley harvest' or the 'month of sowing'. It is more probable that the term refers to 'appointed' seasons—i.e. festivals, etc. The word (mo'ed) is used throughout the Old Testament for feasts, solemn days, set times, appointed times and even appointed places such as the tabernacle. If so, we have once again the provision made by God for something which would be required centuries later. This principle—so often overlooked—runs through God's work. He has a purpose in everything even though the fulfilment of that purpose may apparently be long delayed.

These heavenly bodies are also given for 'signs'. The word means 'evidence—proof—token'. Primarily the sun and moon are evidence of the creatorial power and wisdom of God . . . the heavens declare the glory of God! They are used, too, as evidence of the enduring character of God . . . 'as long as the sun and moon shall endure'. Even though the sun uses up $\frac{1}{4}$ million tons of matter in a minute, transforming it to energy, there is reason to believe that it can maintain this for 50,000 million years—and calculation shows that the sun would still have the greater part of its mass left then!

But the sun and moon have also been reserved by the Creator

for special 'signs'. By a control of the apparent position in the sky of the sun in the reign of Hezekiah a special message was given to that monarch. In the times of Amos, and possibly on other occasions, an eclipse of the sun or moon became a prophetic warning. At the birth of Christ the appearance of a new star, comet, or other celestial body, probably coinciding with the very rare conjunction of the planets Jupiter and Saturn in the constellation of Pisces (which according to Abarbanel occurred also before the birth of Moses) was the divinely-appointed sign to the eastern Magi of the approach of the most important event that had thus far occurred on this little planet. Deeply symbolic, too, were those three hours of darkness, stranger and far longer than any total eclipse of the sun, which enshrouded the Saviour of the world as He completed a task more mighty even than that of making suns or moons.

And there are many who, reading what is said of the last days, think that our planet's run of great stability will be modified by some considerable astronomical upheavals which will be the sign or evidence that the Creator has resumed direct physical intervention in the world which He created but which has largely rejected or ignored Him.

CHAPTER 14

THE FIFTH DAY—AQUATIC LIFE

And God said,
> Let the waters bring forth abundantly
> the moving creature
> that hath life,
> and let fowl fly above the earth
> in the open firmament of heaven.

Gen. I. 20

ON Day 5 the account returns to the study of the oceans and the atmosphere, whose earlier stages have already been described on Day 2. The populating of these with living creatures is now the all-important theme. Life must exist not only on the land but in the sky and in the oceans. This is essential for the overall balance of life on the planet.

Our early forefathers must often have pondered the question of the origin of marine and bird life. Might not these creatures be worthy of their worship? Were they ruled by Dagon or Neptune or some god of the sea? Could the hawk and the ibis be the representatives of divine beings?

If, in the vast scheme of nature, it was necessary for the Creator to plan and produce birds and fishes, it was equally necessary in the dogmatic revelation made in Genesis for Him to assert that these forms of life were only a part of His handiwork. Sea monsters or sparrows, whales or willow warblers, *tannim* or tits—all were part of His great creation, planned, completed and revealed. There was, and is, only one God.

We turn first, then, to the description of aquatic life. Our attention is drawn by the text to several points.

1. The ability of the creatures to move
2. Their 'creation'
3. The great number of these creatures
4. Their character as 'living souls'
5. The very large size of some of them.

Our English version says that the waters were to bring forth abundantly the moving creatures. It may be recalled that in the case of grass and trees the original text spoke of the earth as 'sprouting sproutage' or 'vegetating vegetation'. The verb and the noun were almost identical. So it is again in the text before us. Let the waters swarm (with) swarmers or teem (with) teemers. The essential idea behind the word is undoubtedly that of multitude; the second idea is that the individuals are moving about. The word 'swarm' is not used for fixed things like trees but for such creatures as frogs (Exodus 8. 3). We note, then, the first points about the aquatic creatures; they were to be numerous and mobile. This ability to move is mentioned again in v. 21— 'every living creature that moveth'—with a different Hebrew word from the 'swarmers' of the previous verse. Taking a wide general view it is true that so-called animal life is differentiated from plant life by ability to move about. Admittedly as we now define and classify things there are a few members of the animal kingdom which lead a more or less fixed life and some species from the vegetable domain which move about; but the Genesis account is not aiming at twentieth century classification but the best overall picture for general readers. It is certain that the vast majority of common forms of life can be divided into the fixed and the movable, and these are approximately co-extensive with the vegetable and animal realms. Of the ability of most forms of aquatic life to move few will need to be reminded. One has only to watch the incessant dartings of the sticklebacks and minnows or the goldfish of an aquarium, or to watch the beautiful movements of the herring, the plaice or even the turtle, to see it for oneself. Baby porpoises have been observed swimming alongside their mothers, keeping pace with a 15-knot ship. Full grown porpoises have been seen to do forty miles an hour! No one has recorded the longest ocean voyages made by the inhabitants of the deep, but at mating time some of them do thousands of miles to their breeding-places. They certainly are 'moving' creatures.

Our attention is next drawn to the process of their appearance on the earth. In verse 20 God says, 'Let the waters swarm with swarms'. In verse 21, 'God created' the marine creatures. The first expression seems to imply that they were produced by some natural forces operating in the oceans. The second seem to imply that the creatures would still not have arisen but for God's over-ruling control of those forces. This seems to be in essence the Christian position with regard to any theories of creature formation whether by evolution or some other process. On the material side the scientist may examine the forces that seem to be in operation and may attempt to track their paths. On the other side the Christian, while welcoming such enquiry, will still insist that the overall plan lay, not in the blind forces of the atoms, but in the mind of a supreme Creator.

In verse 12 the earth puts forth or brings forth plants, in verse 20 the waters swarm with, or bring forth abundantly marine life. In verse 24 the earth brings forth animal life. In Job even the oceans are brought forth and in Psalm 90 the hills are brought forth. There is a unity of plan in a diversity of operations. Different natural forces have been used for each of these. While from the scientific aspect these things happen as a result of natural processes most of which are still beyond us to unravel, yet to the Hebrew—and to the Christian—these are creatorial acts of God. It is worth repeating that the word *bara'* 'to create', has a far vaster and wider meaning than has commonly been attributed to it, and therein lies part of the cause of the frequent arguments between scientists and Christians; both are looking at the same wall but they are looking at opposite sides of it.

God, then, created the sea creatures. How He did it, or from the scientific side, what forces produced these creatures is not revealed in the text and is equally unknown to science. On purely scientific grounds alone we must reject the utter nonsense about the sea becoming so thick with nitrogen compounds that by chance some molecules linked up to make proteins endowed with the wonderful power of forcing their way upwards to produce plants, fishes, birds, reptiles, mammals and man!

The text of Genesis 1 does not discuss the changing forms of marine life through the geological ages. We can only conclude from the fossil record that they did change and that some of the earlier forms have now become extinct, while other forms have survived with surprisingly little change, as for example the coelocanth,[1] during the course of 70 million years. The Christian

---

[1] The coelocanths existed in the Cretaceous . . . but apparently not later! The specimen Latimeria found off Madagascar is believed to have come from a depth of 200 fathoms of salt water—yet cretaceous specimens were believed to have been freshwater fish. J. S. Coleman, *The Sea and its Mysteries*, p. 141. The False Killer whale 'Pseudoria crassidens' was also supposed extinct since Pliocene times yet a number have been observed over the last 40 years. Ibid., p. 140.

may accept that many of these forms arose by the modification of others over long periods; that the new forms better suited the newer conditions and that sometimes the older forms were no longer desirable in the changed environment and hence died out. He also observes that some forms seem to have arisen rapidly in large numbers, and as the Christian is not tied down to any theory of evolution, he is in the happy and truly scientific position of being able to await further discoveries. He need not waste his time inventing most unlikely hypothetical links between extinct forms which are widely different. He is not tied, as so many evolutionists are tied, to the dogmatic belief that life arose only once and that all present forms of life must be traced back to that one form. To him, God was able to use 'natural' forces several or even many times over long ages to introduce new forms of life. The God who could design deep sea prawns[1] that change their forms completely five times in one little lifetime could certainly arrange for a given species to undergo a relatively rapid modification better suited to a new environment when He so willed. The Christian, then, need not rule out modification in descent; the evolutionists should not rule out the overriding control of a Creator who works to a design.

A special command was given to these aquatic creatures. They were to be fruitful and multiply and fill the waters. They were to be in fact 'swarming' creatures. Modern studies have revealed something of the extent of this multiplication and of the incredible scheme for supplying food for these hosts.

So far as the mere production of eggs is concerned, apart from the question of fertilizing them, the figures are astounding. The Atlantic salmon produces 15,000 eggs, the herring 30,000. The cod produces from 6 million to 10 million eggs, while the ling is credited with 150 million and the ocean sunfish with 300 million. Naturally few of these hatch out and many of the offspring are eaten by others, but still the numbers of fish in shoals is frequently beyond estimation. An airman is reported to have seen a shoal of fish in the Red Sea 17 miles long. In 1882 a strange fate overtook some of the North Atlantic tile fish and it was estimated that 100 million dead fish were scattered over an area of 5,000 square miles of sea. The quantities of fish caught by men are prodigious.

---

[1] e.g. The deep sea prawn Sergestes atlanticus.

Estimates like 17 million tons annually have been given. American fisheries claim 100,000 tons of haddock alone each year. Perhaps stranger are the records of Japanese fishers whose hauls include 70,000 tons annually of the octopus family[1] . . . prized as a delicacy!

With the realization of the vastness of the population of the sea there comes also a realization of the problem of feeding these hosts.[2] The sharks may eat the cod and the cod may eat the herring but what does the herring eat? The herring eats a mixed diet of smaller fry from the so-called plankton. A single herring may have in its stomach as many as 6,000 tiny creatures, mostly crustaceans of fantastic appearance when seen under a microscope. But what do these copepods live on? They eat the tiny plants—diatoms, algae, etc.—the 'pastures of the sea', and one copepod may require 100,000 diatoms for a meal![3] The human mind reels at the astronomical numbers of diatoms and other minute plants required to keep going the life-cycle of the oceans. Ultimately, too, the diatoms must feed, for they are plants and must draw their food from somewhere. But all is provided. The atmosphere provides the oxygen and carbon dioxide and the rivers bring from the continental rocks the phosphates and silicates and other constituents necessary for the little plants and incidentally the calcium necessary for the hard parts of the innumerable foraminifera and crustaceans and molluscs. Sometimes, when ancient stretches of sea have dried up, they have left behind them empty boxes in which the diatoms lived. This wonderful powder, Kieselguhr, may have 400 million diatom cases to the cubic yard.

The aquatic animals are described by the writer in Genesis 1 as 'having life'. In the Hebrew it is 'living souls'. This word *nephesh* i.e. soul, seems to mean primarily 'that which breathes' or 'a breathing thing', but on numerous occasions it means no more than a 'being'. Thus we read in Numbers 31. 35 of 32,000

---

[1] The Ceylon Pearl fishery is said to account for 80 million oysters a year. E. Boulenger, *A Natural History of the Seas*, p. 99.

[2] It is estimated that half the total photosynthetic fixation of CO_2 into organic matter, equivalent to 1.5×10^{11} tons of carbon a year, is brought about by the marine plankton and algae!

[3] Besides diatoms there are minute flagellates. In 1947 these caused the 'red tide' along the shores of W. Florida. 1 pint of water contained 60 million flagellates, and they were responsible for the death of over 50 million fishes.

'souls' and in 35. 11 of killing any 'soul'. In Genesis 1. 30 all the animal, but none of the vegetable, creation is classified as living *nephesh* or soul. In Genesis 2. 7 we find that it requires a special act of the Creator, described under the figure of God breathing into him, to endow man with this 'breathing being'—to make him a living soul. No such provision is made for fishes and birds or land animals, so that it would seem that the 'soul' of man must truly be regarded as in some essential way different from the soul of the animals.

When the Genesis account proceeds to the actual fulfilment of the Divine plan we are told:

> 'And God created great whales (R.V. sea monsters)
> And every living creature that moveth
> which the waters brought forth abundantly. . . .'

Attention is plainly directed to the great size of these. The '*tannim*' are the 'long extended things', for so the Hebrew means, although a very similar word is used for 'to howl' and hence for the jackal. In a verse like Lamentations 4. 3 it is difficult to decide whether the text should read: 'Even the sea monsters give suck to their young' . . . which is true of whales, dugongs and manatees, or 'even the jackals suckle their young'. But in Genesis 1 there is no doubt that the word refers to the 'long, extended things'. It might be tempting to suppose that the passage referred to the great reptiles of the Triassic period which some believe are descended from great marine creatures, but it seems more reasonable to suppose that the passage refers to great sea creatures known to and co-eval with man. The seas surrounding the Middle East would have provided him with sufficient of these even if we omit those seen by travellers. Whales of 40 to 50 feet long may well have been known to the inhabitants of Bible lands and of course, so far as the world as a whole is concerned, such would be small. The blue whale (Balaenoptera musculus) has been known to exceed 100 feet. A specimen stranded at Ostend measured 102 feet. Mother whales of this species always exceed 75 feet and the largest foetus recorded was 27 feet. The mothers supply milk with 10 times the fat contents of cow's milk and sometimes suckle babies till they are 50 feet long! The whale-shark, too, was once common in the Mediterranean, its teeth being still found in the mud. The white shark (Carcharodon) may reach 40 feet and the whale-shark (Rhineodon) may reach 60 feet. The sea has other 'long extended things' or *tannim* . . . there is the octopus with a span up to 40 feet and the giant squid (Architeuthis princeps, probably the largest living invertebrate) with a body 12 feet long and arms 30-40 feet and a total weight of 2 tons. It is true that some jelly fish 8 feet across and with tentacles 120 feet long have been recorded but as these are largely water the true body weight is small. Still there is no doubt that the oceans contain many 'long extended creatures'.

As with the heavens themselves so the living things provide astounding evidence of the power of the Creator and the vast range of His work. The great blue roqual 90-100 feet long and 150 tons in weight is probably one hundred thousand million times the size of the ocean's diatoms. Yet the diatoms and similar tiny plants are the ultimate source of food not only for whales but for all other marine creatures.

> Yonder is the sea, great and wide,
> Wherein are things creeping innumerable,
> Both small and great beasts . . .
> These wait all upon Thee,
> That Thou mayest give them their meat in due season.
>
> Ps. 104. 25, 27 R.V.

Truly

> Those who go down to great waters
> 'See the works of the Lord,
> And His wonders in the deep,'

—perhaps, when armed with a net and a microscope, in a way far more wonderful than ever the Psalmist dreamed of.

CHAPTER 15

THE FIFTH DAY—BIRDS

'Fowl that may fly above the earth
In the open firmament of heaven . . .
God created . . . every winged fowl
after his kind:
and God saw that it was good.
And God blessed them, saying . . .
Let fowl multiply in the earth.'

Gen. 1. 20-22

WE turn now to the air around us. No part of God's world was
to be left empty. The Creator planned and formed creatures
suited to their environment. They are described by the simple
word *'oph* or fliers. Some[1] have supposed that the word here
refers to flying insects but this seems to be due to a desire to
obtain an exact correspondence between the order in Genesis 1
and that of the fossil record as we now find it. That the word can
be used for insects may be seen from Leviticus 11. 20-23, but
there seems no question that the significance in Genesis 1 is
primarily, if not solely, that of birds. The same word is used in
Genesis 6 and it is difficult to suppose that Noah had to arrange
accommodation in the ark for a hundred thousand different species
of insects some less than ¼ inch long. The word nearly always
refers to birds and will be so taken here. They were to fly in the
open firmament of heaven or perhaps better 'against the face or
expanse of the sky'. So man, indeed, sees them silhouetted
against the 'face of the firmament'. They fly at varying heights
from hedge tops to mountains. Small birds can ascend a few
thousand feet, larger ones to 10,000 feet, and birds have even been
found in mountain areas at 20,000 feet.

We note in passing, once again, the similarity of noun and verb

---

[1] é.g. Prof. A. Rendle Short, in his excellent *Modern Discovery and the Bible*,
Ch. 4.

'oph . . . *'uph* . . . fliers . . . fly. Surely this is another proof that the original account was given in some very early language.

Just as the inhabitants of the deep swim and twist and turn with beautiful grace and speed so these creatures soar or cruise or dive with amazing ease. While many are content with a leisurely 20-30 m.p.h. the somewhat ungainly crow can hurry along at 45 m.p.h. when necessary, and swifts have passed slow-moving aircraft which were registering 70 m.p.h. at 6,000 feet. The maximum speed of birds is not known for certain but it is probable that some reach 100 m.p.h. in dives. Very remarkable, too, is the wonderful power of 'sailing' possessed by such birds as the gull, the vulture and the albatross. This latter great ocean-going bird will 'sail' with and around a ship for half an hour without an apparent stroke of its wings![1] Truly then these 'fliers that fly' belong to the order of 'moving creatures'.

They move, too, in another sense. Very many of them possess the strange power of migration.[2] This power is often described as an 'instinct' and it has never been satisfactorily explained.[3] The rather pathetic attempts to explain it as left over from the early history of the bird race when it had to deal with the ice age can be seen in the *Encyclopaedia Britannica*.[4] The pattern of migration is too wonderful to be explained in terms of recollections of ancestral efforts to avoid colder regions. It is too wonderful for any simple, single explanation. That the actual mechanism is based on chemical or physical causes in the birds, triggered perhaps by something in the environment, on the material side, is obvious, and scientists should search for, and may find, it. But on the Christian side there is still the wonder at the over-all plan in the mind of the Creator who 'built in' such a mechanism into birds . . . a mechanism which guides the Golden Plover from the Arctic to the Argentine—sometimes across 2,000 miles

---

[1] A 20lb. albatross may have a skeleton weighing under 3 lb., so wonderful is its weight to strength ratio. Its wing span of up to 12 feet gives it a lift to drag ratio equal to the best man-made sail planes, but in its use of these wings it makes the human constructions appear crude and clumsy. It can average 40 m.p.h. and usually keeps within the 30-58 m.p.h. range. W. Jameson, *The Wandering Albatross.*

[2] Migration is very noticeable among birds but it also occurs among whales, seals, fish, bats, butterflies, locusts and dragonflies.

[3] All explanations are rejected, for example, by B. Vesey-Fitzgerald in *Background to Birds*. Birds may use sun and stars for direction.

[4] 14th Edition 1929.

of ocean,[1] which guides some small birds to find a relatively tiny island like Hawaii in the vast Pacific ocean, or the N. European Stork to undertake a journey of 6,000 miles to S. Africa. When we remember that in some cases the young birds of the new generation actually migrate before their parents and sometimes choose a safer route than that taken by older birds—to arrive at the same destination—and yet when they grow older follow the more difficult route leaving the next generation to start off on the safer one . . . then we must confess that for the moment we have reached an unsolved mystery.[2] And should scientists at last unravel the complicated mechanism behind the mystery we shall surely be staggered in amazement at the wonder of the Mind of the Potter who put such an intricate device into such tiny pots.

We are given in Genesis 1 no explanation as to how birds arose in the earth. The text is content to tell us that, along with fishes, they were created by God. Scientifically we are no better off. We can of course study birds and weigh and measure and count and describe them. We can study them alive or dead, and compare present birds with fossilized remains. We can say, to take just one example, that on a crane's feather there are some 600 fine shafts (or barbs) on either side of the central rib, and that each of these carries about 600 pairs of smaller shafts (barbules) making over a million of these on one feather . . . and that these are perfectly designed with little sets of hooks capable of interlocking when the feather is in use. Then we can conclude with the atheist that this wonderful scheme arose by chance or we can conclude with the Christian that it is the product of a Mind far more wonderful than our own. The fantastic speculations of some evolutionists can be seen in the *Encyclopaedia Britannica*[3] where early reptiles are pictured as practising 'swift runs with long leaps into the air' while others 'parachuted from tree to tree'. The idea of countless

---

[1] The great albatross has been seen at sea 2,000 miles from the nearest nesting island.

[2] The 'Monarch' or Milkweed butterflies spend the winter resting on trees (sometimes thousands on one tree) in Mexico, Florida and S. California, preferably near the coast. With spring they set off one by one northward laying eggs as they go. According to the distance they have flown to the north there are three generations, two, or one before the autumn return to the south. It is the children, grandchildren or great grandchildren of the butterflies that flew north that fly south again in the autumn. C. B. Williams, *Journal of the Royal Society of Arts*, No. 4711, February 1946, p. 178.

[3] 14th Edition, 1929.

generations of these creatures practising long jumps for some millions of years before becoming birds with feathers is too utterly absurd for words. Are we likewise to believe that for thousands of years caterpillars did faster and faster runs followed by flying leaps until they became butterflies? May we not rather recognize that the Creator Who has designed caterpillars with a marvellous 'built in' mechanism which enables them to turn into butterflies in one complete metamorphosis, could also have designed some earlier creatures on this earth which, at some stage in the world's history, underwent a similar drastic change, producing in a relatively short time birds with all the new apparatus for flying complete? Surely, indeed, birds were either created by some such planned controlled metamorphosis . . . from a reptilian or other stock, or else de novo!

The text of Genesis 1 emphasizes that God created 'every fowl . . . after his kind'. No number of such kinds is given although throughout the Bible some twenty-five to thirty groups are named.[1] There are in the world some 8-10,000 species of birds which can be grouped into about thirty 'orders'. Even in geological times many birds existed, the oldest going back to Jurassic times. Some hundreds of fossil species are on record, some of them still being represented today.

In size there is not the vast range that characterized the inhabitants of the sea, unless indeed we include insects with the 'fliers'. Of true birds the smallest is the little Cuban Humming Bird said to weigh 1/10 oz. and to be $2\frac{1}{4}$ inches long. The Condor has a span of 9 feet and the Albatross up to 12 feet. The Emperor Penguin stands 4 feet high, the Emu 5 feet and the Ostrich— which may weigh up to 300 lb.—7 feet. The Moa, which became extinct in New Zealand in relatively recent times, was 10-12 feet high and the Elephant Bird (Aepyornis), which lived several centuries ago in Madagascar, reached 11 feet and laid a 13-inch egg.

Finally the record tells us that the Creator endowed these creatures also with the power of multiplication—reproduction— in the earth. In the earth: because although some birds spend much of their time near the sea and albatrosses and petrels seem to live at sea, yet all come to land at some time, especially for

---

[1] See Prof. G. Driver, *Pal. Expl. Quarterly*, April and Oct. 1955. The Hebrew names are not co-extensive exactly with modern species or families.

nesting, and the vast majority do belong to the earth rather than to the sea.

They are theoretically capable of multiplying at a prodigious rate but in actual fact the population is greatly reduced by a very high mortality rate. The common Blackbird may have three broods, each of four or five young, in a year but of these fifteen some will die soon after leaving the nest and others will have but a very short life. If this were not so the numbers of birds would soon run into millions of millions. Local illustrations of this great fertility are occasionally observed when one species multiplies rapidly in a given region. There was, for example, the strange case of the Passenger Pigeon which was said at times to have darkened the skies in places in the United States. One town in 1869 is recorded as sending 11 million to market in a year. Yet the last surviving Passenger Pigeon died in captivity in 1914, and the species is now extinct! There are accounts, too, of great congregations of ducks known as 'rafts' in some of which it was estimated that there were 100,000 birds. Truly they have multiplied in the earth and many pairs even go so far as to map out and defend their own little 'territory' into which they refuse to allow another similar pair to come. They have taken the whole planet as their parish. From the little Terns of the Arctic to the Vulture of the wilderness, from the Penguins of the Antarctic to the Toucans and Parrots of the Tropics, from the Albatrosses of the distant oceans to Ostriches of the savannahs—the birds have indeed fulfilled the intention of the Creator that they should multiply in the earth.

Their tasks are many. Some are nature's scavengers; others carry seeds to distant parts and become God's gardeners. While their own numbers are kept severely in check they themselves largely control that vast army of smaller workers—the insects—which, if left unchecked, would ruin the world in less than ten years. 'Birds', said Michelet, 'can live without man, but man cannot live without birds'.[1] The *Encyclopaedia Britannica* contains an estimate that the Thrushes of the British Isles consume 3,000,000,000 insects and grubs in three months.[2]

Although every year the mortality rate among sparrows is

---

[1] Quoted in J. A. Thomson, *The Biology of Birds*, 1923, p. 414.
[2] *Enc. Brit.* Vol. 16 (1929), p. 934. Art. Ornithology.

about 50%, yet the Creator who made them is also the Heavenly Father Who notes their fall. It must needs be so. Once a race of creatures has the power to multiply by giving birth to numerous offspring then death must inevitably be introduced to maintain the balance. What is true of the birds is true of all animal and vegetable life . . . given birth, death is inevitable. Only to man, made in the image of God, was a different story possible. Yet even he rejected the way of life and brought death upon himself till One Greater Man, through death itself, restored the way to that Life which death can never end. We are to Him of more value than many sparrows.

CHAPTER 16

THE SIXTH DAY— THE LAND ANIMALS

And God said,
> Let the *earth* bring forth the living creature
> after its kind,
>   (a) cattle,
> and (b) creeping thing,
> and (c) beast of the earth . . . after its kind:
> and it was so.
> And God made
>   (c) the beast of the earth . . . after its kind,
> and (a) cattle   . . . after their kind,
> and (b) everything that creepeth
>   upon the ground . . . after its kind:
> and God saw that it was good.   Gen. 1. 24-25 R.V.

WE have here the same typical forms of poetical pattern that have been seen so clearly in the earlier sections. We see also that Day 6 has returned to the study of the land which was last considered on Day 3. Then, just as Day 3 dealt with two major topics, the dry land itself and vegetation, so now Day 6 is concerned with two great subjects, land animals and man.

As we consider the land animals two questions are brought before us. What categories of animals are included in each of the sub-sections above? How were these creatures produced on the earth?

The basis of the classification of the animals does not seem easy to determine, mainly by reason of the fact that the terms used overlap in the later passages of the Bible. It might even be that the 'beasts of the earth' is the general term for the two subsections 'cattle' (a) and 'creeping things' (b). It would seem, however, more probable that the land animals are considered under three headings:

(a) behemah—from the root 'to be dumb', i.e. 'dumb animals'
    =approximately cattle and the larger herbivorous animals.

(b) remes—creepers,
 =approximately the smaller animals, weasels, stoats, mice,
 rabbits, etc.
(c) chaytho 'erets—beasts of the earth,
 =approximately the wilder animals not listed above.

We find that in later passages of the Bible group (a) includes
not only cattle but horses, mules and asses; that it includes clean
as well as unclean beasts and that it can include the larger
carnivora, for the lion is spoken of as the king among them.
In Leviticus 11. 29 such creatures as mice and lizards are grouped
with the 'remes'. The third term can be used for land animals in
general, but the context here seems to limit it to the remaining
beasts of the earth whether carnivorous or not.

Such a classification of the land animals seems extremely
simple; the biologists might term it crude. Yet it is far more
suitable for the general reader than any list of zoological orders.
It must needs be so. Any attempt to list even the chief orders of
land animals would be quite out of place here. The text gives
the impression that terrestrial creatures of every kind are to be
included. In other words the passage, by using the three-fold
sub-division of animals, succeeds more definitely than it would by
using one general term in conveying the great truth that all land
animals are but part of the creatorial work of God. Two other
simple truths follow. Neither apes nor bulls nor pythons are
worthy of worship—although numerous ancient peoples thought
that they were. Neither apes nor bulls nor any other creatures
have arisen on this earth by the operation of blind chance—
although some atheistical evolutionists may have thought that
they did. The second question before us concerns once again the
mode of formation of these beasts. On the one hand the passage
assures us that, as before, the over-all power and pattern are
God's and His alone. On the other hand—the scientific side—the
text boldly asserts that God empowered the earth to 'bring forth'
these creatures. The process of 'bringing forth' is the completion
of a long story of gradual development—not random but controlled
—from the very simple to the very complex. Time and orderly
development are essentially involved in 'bringing forth'. The
inspired writer is guided to this figure of speech all the way
through the story to rule out the idea of the instantaneous creation
of each type of animal from inorganic matter . . . an idea beloved

of some expositors. As natural forces operating along the lines designed by the Creator over a considerable period of weeks or months shape and build the creature that is at last 'brought forth' by its mother, so in the development of this earth natural forces, operating along lines designed by the Creator, have shaped and moulded and built the vast succession of creatures intended to live here.[1] To the geologist it seems that at certain times fairly rapid changes set in among certain species so that the older forms died out and completely new forms emerged, sometimes with little evidence of intermediate types, as if the race had suddenly undergone some change vaguely resembling the metamorphosis of an individual. The parallel cannot, of course, be pressed too closely. At other times much slower changes took place and the fossil records reveal several stages of a gradual modification. Very little is known of the cause of all this. The modification of some specks of matter called genes, the alteration of the chemical linkages of some complex nucleic acids and adjacent proteins may be some of the factors involved. A very small alteration at this molecular level makes an immense difference at the level of species and orders. What, on the natural side, controls or triggers these rearrangements we do not know. But we do know that the earth has obeyed the command[2] and that it has produced—brought forth—an incredible succession and an immense variety of forms of life, so that even among land mammals alone we have a range from mice to mammoths.

---

[1] Scientists, keeping only to the material side of this story, as indeed they must, have called the 'bringing forth' of living creatures, evolution. The Christian, like the author of Genesis 1, sees all this as part of the guided and controlled work of God.

[2] The guiding power being still that Spirit of God which brooded over the original chaos.

CHAPTER 17

THE SIXTH DAY—MAN

And God said,
Let us make man
in our image,
after our likeness:
and let them have dominion — — —
and God created man
in His own image,
in the image of God
created He him;
male and female
created He them.
And God blessed them:
and God said,
Be fruitful, and multiply,
and fill the earth,
and subdue it;
and have dominion — — —

Gen. i. 26-28

WE come now to the climax of creation's story. Not indeed from the point of astronomy or geology or even biology. Stars and mountains and prehistoric beasts could exist without man. But so far as the Book is concerned, and so far as we its readers are concerned, we have come to the climax. The Book is the story of one race of beings on one planet in one age. The planet was now established . . . prepared. All was ready and from now to the end of the Book it is the story of God and His creature—man.[1]

And so once again God spoke. Yet at once we are challenged by the absolute difference between the Divine utterance and all that had gone before. God now takes counsel with Himself . . . let Us make man!

---

[1] 'For Albert Vandel, a panoramic view of the history of life leads to the conclusion that man seems to be not only the consummation of evolution but, even more, that all evolution seems to have developed in relation to man, that is to say that it has had as its aim the appearance on the earth of an individual with a large brain, with an intelligence much more developed than that of the most intelligent of animals. And this individual is man.'—Andre Senet. Translated by Malcolm Barnes, *Man in Search of his Ancestors*, p. 267.

We have not, so far, paused to examine the title that the Creator has used for Himself. It was there, back in verse 1. In the beginning God . . . 'elohim. Even in the first verse the title 'elohim[1] was plural yet the verb—created—was singular. But now we have plural throughout most of the verse. Let us (plural) make (plural) man in our (plural) image (singular). God is spoken of some 250 times in the Old Testament as 'el (singular) but around 2,500 times as 'elohim (plural) and that frequently with plural verbs and adjectives though sometimes with singular verbs. Evidently, then, even in the opening lessons of the Bible the readers are being taught something about the nature of the Creator Himself as well as something about His work. His Being is so wonderful as to require both singular and plural words. Hear, O Israel, the Lord (Jehovah) our God ('elohim, plural) is one Lord (Jehovah). Deut. 6. 4.

Various efforts have been made to do away with the obvious implications of such grammatical forms. Some have suggested that the form used is the plural of 'self-deliberation', but this will not explain the hundreds of occasions when 'elohim is used with no question of self-deliberation. Others have suggested that this is the Royal Plural or plural of majesty or excellence. But the plural of majesty is used by the king usually when speaking on behalf of his people collectively . . . as their representative . . . or when speaking to them. Thus our Queen says, 'We will do this or that' and she speaks of 'our children and our home'. But the sentences then are consistently plural. The Queen does not say, 'We am going to Canada'. In Genesis 1 'elohim is used not only by God in the first person but also of Him in the third person and even back in verse 1, as we have seen, with a singular verb created.[2] The suggestion that God is addressing the angels or speaking on behalf of the angels fails utterly. Man is not made in the image of the angels[3] nor had angels any share in creating man. The expression 'our' image cannot possibly be applied to God and the angels together. Weakest of all is the suggestion that the plural

---

[1] We must remember that in Hebrew plural stands for three or more. Two would be dual. Surely God designed even the language that He intended to use.

[2] Dillmann concludes that the idea of plural of majesty is inconsistent with Hebrew idiom. The idea grew up either as representing the king collectively for his people or possibly the blasphemous attempts of potentates to seize the form of title due to God alone.

[3] In Heb. 2. 16 angelic nature is actually contrasted with human nature.

forms are left over from the polytheism of some Babylonian myths which the Jewish writers have failed to translate into the singular. *'elohim* (plural) is found, not only in Genesis 1, but at the other end of the Old Testament in Malachi 3 to say nothing of 2,500 other times throughout the book.[1]

There remains no alternative but to recognize the full force of the teaching of the whole of the Old Testament that God cannot adequately be described by the use of the singular alone. His Nature contains that which essentially demands in our human speech the use of the plural. Let *us* make man! It remains for the New Testament to reveal more of that mysterious plurality in unity as it unveils the Only Begotten Son upon whom rested the Holy Spirit. This, then, is the Creator . . . *God* plural . . . Who after self-deliberation worked, if we might so speak, together to make man. 'Let us make man in our image'. Little wonder, then, that in the rest of the Book, Father, Son and Spirit work together for the redemption of the prodigal race of Adam.

Let us turn now to the creature . . . *man* . . . *'adam*. The Hebrew language is rich in words for man. There is *'ish*, the husband or male, *'enosh* the mortal man, *ba'al* the master or lord, *gibbor* the valiant man and even *nephesh* a soul or being, but here it is *'adam*, i.e. *man* as a race. It is a singular noun, collective for all. In Hebrew it has no plural. The word is common throughout the Old Testament where it occurs some 560 times and in its last reference it shows the gulf between man and God for Malachi 3. 8 reads, 'Will a man rob God'? Its root is still uncertain. *'adom* also means 'Red' and *'adamah* means earth or ground and it might easily be that Man is regarded as derived from red earth.[2] In Chapter 2 the name becomes the proper name of an individual— the man.[3] In Chapter 3 the references are mainly to the individual but in Chapter 6. 1 the *'adam* began to multiply and we read of the daughters of *'adam* i.e. of man. In Chapter 6. 7 God says that He will destroy Man (*'adam*) from the earth, although of course Noah was preserved from this punishment. In Chronicles 1. 1

---

[1] Apart from the absurdities of this 'Babylonian Hypothesis' it is interesting to note that in the Babylonian legend Marduk uses the singular:
I shall make man . . .
I shall create . . .
[2] Some derive it from a root meaning 'to produce'.
[3] See chapter 2 verse 15 margin, verse 19 and verse 20.

the word is plainly a proper name once more . . . *Adam*, Sheth, Enosh. So God created Man . . . that is, the race.[1] It is true that in a special sense He created the first man, who takes the racial name Adam, but in so doing God, in effect, created the race and we are all His creatures and are commanded to remember our Creator.

This race, this being, *Man*, was to be superior to all other orders of creation so far dealt with. Let us, says God, make man in our *image*, after our *likeness*. Some have thought that the 'image' and the 'likeness' represent two different truths, the image being constitutional and the likeness external or acquired. Others feel that the Hebrew use of parallel expressions for emphasis demands that the two terms should cover almost the same area of significance. The word 'likeness' is the easier of the two. Its simple meaning in the Hebrew is adequately expressed by the English words, likeness, resemblance or similitude (Daniel 10. 16, cf. James 3. 9). But for the second term the Hebrews have six quite different words which can be translated *image*. The one used in Genesis 1. 26, *tselem* is very often used in the Old Testament for the images of heathen gods. These were supposed by the heathen to represent the presence of the god among his people. The image was worshipped—it was the visible representation of the god. Such was, of course, anathema to the True and Only God. He made *Man*, and man only, to be in His image— His visible regent over creation—and man could not give away that position to stocks or stones or birds, beasts or fishes. Even if man threw away the honour heaped upon him, and marred the image, God's purpose could not change. No idol image could ever be tolerated. The image that man marred, though never completely lost, must ultimately be restored in *Man*.

> ' . . . till one greater Man
> Restore us, and regain the blissful seat.'
>
> . . . . . .
>
> A fairer Paradise is founded now
> For Adam and his chosen Sons, whom thou
> A Saviour art come down to re-install.'
> *Paradise Lost*, Book 1, line 4. *Paradise Regained*, Book 4, line 613-5.

---

[1] We have thus once again the extension of the use of a word. Adam stands first for one man, then for the whole race. Compare the extension of the words earth and heaven. We have also extended the meaning of the word father to mean an ancestor, and of son to mean a descendant.

That perfect image of God is seen complete, restored, not in an angel or an archangel, not in a cherub or a seraph, but in Jesus Christ . . . a perfect *Man*.

We must, however, come back to the question 'Wherein lies this difference between *Man* and the brute'? 'How is man in the image and after the likeness of God'? To be in the image of God demands some essential resemblances however remote the ultimate gap may be. The vice-regent must have something in common with the One on the throne, both in nature and power. If the King is capable of self-deliberation, of intelligent planning and the execution of His plan then, on a smaller scale, so must the 'images' be. If He creates, so on a lesser scale must they, by forming and fashioning new things. If He controls and directs, so must they. If He possesses the Absolute Will, so must man have some degree of freedom of will. If God rules, so must Adam.

The image is not in itself the possession of dominion but the two are inseparably linked. Being God's image . . . His visible representation on earth . . . man must have dominion otherwise he is no true representative, and thus this authority is at once conferred upon him. Dominion over all living[1] things is his. It lies beyond the confines of this work to ask how far man lost this image and likeness at the fall; that he is still regarded as being in the image of God can be seen, not only after the flood (Gen. 9. 6) but in the New Testament times, when Paul speaks in 1 Corinthians 11. 7 quite definitely of man as the image of God.[2] The image was doubtless marred; it was never completely lost. It is restored, as we have said, completely in Christ and ultimately in those who are changed into His image.[3]

> So God created man in His own image,
> In the image of God created He him;
> Male and female created He them.

Two great questions occur to our minds. How did God make them? How many individuals did He make in this initial process?

---

[1] Sir J. W. Dawson, *Modern Science in Bible Lands*, p. 34 points out that in Gen. 1. 26 the wild beasts are not included in man's dominion. Yet Psalm 8 seems to imply that the entire animal creation was made subject to man's dominion.

[2] Cf. also Jas. 3. 9; Col. 3. 10.

[3] 2 Cor. 3. 18.

So far as the first question is concerned there is little reason to suspect that we know any more about the creation of man than we know about the creation of animals or plants or matter. We can certainly examine some of the suggestions that have been advanced, but we shall find, as we have found before, that since creation involves scientific processes beyond anything that we have yet understood, the Bible does not attempt to discuss the 'How' of things. Honesty, however, demands that a little later we give consideration to suggestions which have been made.

The second question seems simpler and, so far as the Bible is concerned, the obvious answer seems to be two—Adam and Eve. All their descendants were created by God in a sense but only two individuals are mentioned in the original process. Some have thought otherwise and it will be wise to examine both what the Bible actually does state—and imply—and also what facts anthropology, geology and archaeology can put before us. We must evidently clear the ground step by step.

Genesis 1 has a simple, straightforward and very grand style. Its great truths are stated like great monoliths . . . God created! Chapter 2 is written in a different style.[1] It is much more anthropomorphic than Chapter 1. The Lord God is pictured as actually planting a garden, taking Adam and putting him in the garden and then bringing the animals one by one to him. As the creation of man comes in both chapters it may be as well to consider first the relationship between these two chapters.

Some critics[2] have asserted that Genesis 1 was written by an anonymous writer or school of writers, of the Priestly order, somewhere about the time of the Babylonian Exile, while Chapter 2 is said to be the work of another anonymous, but much earlier, writer generally designated[3] J. Endless arguments have raged over

---

[1] Prof. Ridderbos in his *Genesis 1 and Natural Science*, p. 28 says that it is 'probable that Genesis 1 and Genesis 2 were written by two different authors, or to put it otherwise, derived from different centres of transmission. It is hard to believe that the same author should first write Genesis 1 and then Genesis 2.'

'It will, however, certainly be necessary to emphasize strongly the unity of the book of Genesis. In the book as it has been handed down to us Genesis 2 forms the sequel to Genesis 1, and it must have been the intent of the editor that it be so read.'

[2] See E. J. Young, *Introduction to the Old Testament*, for details and refutation of critical theories.

[3] Because he speaks of 'Jehovah'.

these alleged writers . . . to no profit or certainty to anyone. There is not one verse in the Pentateuch whose meaning is for certain any clearer or deeper for all the years of such work. The world could have been spared all the books written about J. E. P. and D. and it would have been no worse off.

That Moses had access to very ancient writings preserved by his own people[1] as well as some, now lost to us, among the Egyptians is highly probable. That he himself was able to make, and to have written down, long addresses the book of Deuteronomy seems to show clearly. That he was capable, under the influence of God's Spirit, of poetic utterance and description of things yet future can also be seen from the closing chapters of Deuteronomy[2] and Psalm 90. That he compiled the book of Genesis is quite a reasonable supposition, and that it was committed to writing at that time is by no means improbable. That it has been subsequently re-written in later forms of Hebrew is also reasonable and that small additional explanations were inserted by these later editors is quite likely. But granted all this we still do not know the original sources of Genesis 1 and 2.

Genesis 1 must necessarily have been given to someone under those deep spiritual influences which we call inspiration in its deepest sense. In the nature of the case there was no human observer of creation. The chapter is too grand, vast and wonderful for any explanation short of divine inspiration.

Genesis 2 might easily be based on the work of one of Adam's early descendants setting down the story as Adam recounted, probably very often, what he knew—of how he found himself in a beautiful spot on earth, able to speak with a Divine visitor who told him what he was to do and who listened, as with quick intuitive perception he coined words to describe the beasts which came before him. Adam would finally tell of a strange unconsciousness which fell upon him and then of the miracle of awakening to find a partner of nature identical with his own and towards whom he felt that attraction which henceforth became the basis of married life.[3] He certainly would not deal with astronomy, biology or

---

[1] Prof. Aalders G.Ch. considers that Genesis 1 was in writing before the time of Moses.

[2] See the great chapter of 'Blessings' Deut. 33. Deut. 34 is a historical note added to complete the Pentateuch. Verse 6 seems to imply that it was written many years later.

[3] Gen. 2. 24.

geology. He became conscious in Eden and there he begins his story and from there he proceeds.[1] But even if the ultimate source of Genesis 2 is Adam himself the chapter as we now have it is plainly not his. Some later writer, possibly after the flood, actually set it down in writing and some of the Babylonians of pre-Abrahamic date may have known of it,[2] and later, Moses was led by God to use this record to follow up the account of the Creation of heaven and earth. We have, then, in the opening section of Genesis two accounts, or tablets,[3] the first entitled:

Generation of Heaven and earth (Gen. 1. to 2. 5) and the second: Book of the generation (history) of Adam. (Gen. 2. 5-5. 1).

The two accounts are complementary. They are plainly set out with a difference of aim and emphasis. So far as man is concerned Genesis 1 shows him in his setting in the world. Genesis 2 deals with man's moral nature and relation to God. We have two accounts but it is absurd to say that they are contradictory. In Genesis 1 the reader seems to be away in space looking down on a tiny planet and watching things appear on it. In Genesis 2-3 the reader seems to be standing behind one of the trees in a garden listening to God and Adam talking to each other.[4]

After this somewhat lengthy digression let us now survey the two accounts of man's creation.

In Gen. 1   God created man . . . male and female.
Gen. 2. 7   The Lord God formed *MAN*
        of the dust of the ground,
    and breathed into his nostrils the breath of life;
    and man became a living soul.
v. 21   And the Lord God caused a deep sleep to fall upon
    the man, and he slept;
    and He took one of his ribs,
    and the rib which He had taken builded He into woman.

We have already stressed that creation is not necessarily an instantaneous process. It is a process—time is not the crucial factor. The product of the process of creation must be something

---

[1] The section ends at Gen. 5. 2.
[2] Cf. the phrase 'When there was no . . .' in Gen. 2. 4-5 and in the Babylonian 'Enuma elish', line 1.
[3] See P. J. Wiseman, *New Discoveries in Babylon about Genesis*.
[4] The story suggests God in 'angelic' form. The theophanies are beyond us to comprehend but some visible form seems to have been present.

which did not exist as such before. This is true of *Man*. God created man and that process included the formation of Eve. It was not the *instantaneous* creation from dust of the first human pair. Genesis 2 amplifies the account of Genesis 1 Man was formed. Of this forming we have already spoken at length. It is the work of the potter—the skilful fashioning of an object to fulfil the pattern in the mind of the Designer. The inspired record in Jeremiah and Romans follows up the metaphor till Potter and clay become symbolic of God and man. The pots are made by the master Potter to a single design with innumerable minor variations. The forming by a potter is not instantaneous creation from nothing. Genesis 2 then adds at least this fact to our understanding of man's creation. It was a formation—not an instantaneous creation from nothing.

But the account in Genesis 2 goes on to add the phrase, 'from the dust of the earth'. Does not this suggest that Genesis 2 pictures God as taking up mud and making a man? To very simple readers it may. To the depraved polytheistic outlook of the early Babylonians—who, as we have suggested, probably had some version of this account—it certainly did, and they picture Marduk[1] as mixing dust on a reed mat[2] and forming mankind. But these are later and are crude misunderstandings of the figure of speech used. The old Hebrew writers themselves did not take so crude and literal a view. Eliphaz the Temanite[3] speaks of those who dwell in houses of clay, whose foundation is dust. Job[4] says, 'Thou hast fashioned me as clay (note the potter-metaphor) wilt Thou bring me into the dust again'. They had realised that man's body was composed of very fine particles. At death it returned to them. This conception of fine dust was the nearest the early Hebrews got to an atomic theory. The verse in Proverbs 8. 26 which speaks of 'the highest part of the dust of the world' is difficult to translate exactly. The word 'dust', there is plural and is rendered in J. N. Darby's translation, as 'particles', while the American S.R.V. gives 'the first of the dust of the world' . . . a kind of prime element in finely divided form. In Isaiah 40. 15 the prophet speaks of the nations as a drop in a bucket . . . as the small dust of the balance . . . again showing a conception of tiny

---

[1] In the so-called Bilingual account of creation, Rogers, *Cuneiform Parallels*, p. 49.
[2] Or 'earth floor'.   [3] Job 4. 19.   [4] Job 10. 9. R.V.

particles which, in the aggregate, would affect a balance but individually would be too small for the Hebrews to weigh. The Hebrews did, in fact, have yet another word for dust, *daq* . . . and Davies in his *Hebrew Lexicon*[1] actually gives this as 'atom'. Admittedly, of course, the word had not its modern significance but it shows that the Hebrews, long before the Greek Atomists, conceived of things being made of very small particles, and Genesis 2 had already stated that man's body was made of such, and not of some mysterious 'vital element' such as that assumed by the alchemists several thousands of years later. It is, of course, true that on the material side man's body is made of nothing but atoms such as are common to this earth. God indeed formed man of the dust of the ground, and in choosing the word 'dust' He allowed for that expansion of meaning of words as knowledge increased. The Bible says that the human body was composed from tiny particles. Today we realise how really tiny those particles are!

But man is more than a body. In the simple, anthropomorphic picture of Genesis 2 the Divine Potter had formed the dust—the clay—into a pot. He had formed man's body but it was lifeless. And so, still maintaining the same simple form of language, the writer tells us that God next breathed into man's nostrils the breath of life and man became, what the marine creatures (Gen. 1. 20-21) and the land animals (Gen. 1. 26) had already become, a living soul or living being. In this section there is nothing to suggest that man is different from the other 'living souls', save that it is to man alone that the Creator personally communicated the 'breath of life'. This at least sets him above the others. But as we have already seen the great difference has already been laid down. Man is already defined in Chapter 1 as God's vice-regent possessing dominion over all other 'living creatures', and this appears in Chapter 2 as well when man assumes his natural right to name all lesser creatures. But further, simple as the account may be, it also proceeds to establish clearly that this living being is of a different order from all others, in that he is capable of

---

[1] B. Davies, *Hebrew and Chaldee Lexicon*. The word *daq* is used in Isa. 29. 5 (R.V.) 'Thy foes shall be like small dust' and in Isa. 40. 15 the A.V. translates it as 'a very little thing'. It is closely associated with the word used in Isa. 40. 22 where God 'stretches out the heaven as a curtain'.—R.V. margin 'gauze'. The stars are like fine dust. The interstellar material is literally very fine dust!

converse with God and of obeying or disobeying the very commands of God Himself.

We must, however, look a little more closely into this account of the origin and nature of man. What has, or is, he beyond the material body? Let us take the words of Genesis 2 in their simplest form and at the material level. God made man's body from dust and breathed into him the breath of life, and he became a living being. On the material side, then, he is a body, made of atoms. But such a body might exist without life—a carefully preserved corpse. A living being is dynamic, not static. A living being is a working machine and it must not only use up energy but it must draw its supply of energy from its surroundings. A corpse cannot draw energy from its surroundings and then use that energy to do useful work, but a living being can. There are various ways in which this might have been achieved but the Creator chose to make us fuel-burning machines. Such a scheme demands fuel, then oxygen for the combustion of the fuel, and then an efficient system of getting the oxygen to the fuel and transforming the energy of combustion into useful work. The fuel is food and God has made adequate provision for the supplying of this. Oxygen carefully diluted with nitrogen is supplied in endless store by the atmosphere. But man must still have a mechanism for bringing fuel and oxygen together. The entire mechanism would take many volumes to describe but two things are absolutely essential—breathing and blood-circulation.

In breathing man takes in at least a pint of air at each breath—much more if he has been hurrying—eighteen breaths a minute—1,000 pints of air an hour, over 500 cubic feet a day. This gets the oxygen into his lungs; the blood carries it further. The red part of the blood consists of tiny cells of perfectly designed shape containing many far smaller molecules of haemoglobin. In the middle of this incredibly complicated molecule there dwells an atom of iron surrounded by four neighbouring nitrogen atoms which are themselves the inner corners of a wonderfully constructed lattice of carbon, hydrogen and oxygen atoms. When ordinary iron rusts, which its surface can do in a few hours on a damp night, part of the process consists of the iron atoms combining with oxygen atoms. But in the story of the blood the iron atoms in the haemoglobin have only a part of a second to release the carbon dioxide which they are removing from areas of burnt fuel and to pick up a fresh supply of oxygen with which they must hurry to some new scene of activity. Some 30 million million of these little red cells travel along incredible tunnels . . . arteries, veins, capillaries . . . whose total length exceeds 60,000 miles. This they do without ceasing until they wear out—only to be replaced by oncoming millions that have been freshly made. As Dr. Moon says in a well-known Fact and Faith film, *Red River of Life*, if any man wants to believe in God he has 30 million million reasons for doing so in his own blood stream.

All this is, of course, very well known to modern science. It is interesting to observe that the Bible, from its earliest chapters, insists that the secret of life is in two things . . . breath and blood. The life of the flesh is in the blood. God breathed into man and he became a living being.

But this is not the end of the story. With the development of self-consciousness man came to realise that in his essential nature he was more than just atoms and energy, but his problem was how to describe and name his inner essential part. Once again God teaches by expanding the meaning of a word. Man knew that air or wind was the thinnest, finest material . . . it was invisible yet powerful. So the word for wind, *ruach*, became also the word for *spirit*. Even today our word *spirit* is derived from the Latin *spiro*, to breathe. The analogy is maintained in the New Testament as well as the Old. In John 3 our Lord Himself says to Nicodemus, 'The *wind* bloweth where it listeth, so is everyone that is born of the *spirit*'; and in John 20. 22 He *breathed* on His disciples and said, 'Receive ye the *Holy Spirit*'. And when that Holy Spirit came (Acts 2. 2) there was a sound of a rushing, mighty *wind*. Thus wind, air and breath—the invisible sources of life became, and still are, the symbols of that inner essential part of us that lies beyond the realm of matter. Man, *'adam*, then is by nature not only a material body fashioned by the Creator from atoms but he is a living soul, drawing life not only from air but ultimately from the very breath of God Himself. In conclusion, too, it is worthy of note that just as the first man, Adam, was formed by the action of the 'breath of God' upon a divinely-fashioned body, so when the 'second man', the last Adam (1 Cor. 15. 45-47) Jesus Christ came into the world He came into a material body which was divinely prepared through the virgin Mary, but which was quickened by the Holy Spirit who came upon her.

In Genesis 1. 27 we are simply told that when God created man in His image He created 'them' male and female. Genesis 2 in its very different, though homely, style adds somewhat to this very brief account. Man, God's regent over the animal creation, looked around him and devised names for the various creatures, but he could see no one with whom he could hold converse, no one with whom he could share his thoughts, his joys or his dominion. Truly, had he been allowed to continue thus he might well have said:

> I am monarch of all I survey;
>   My right there is none to dispute;
> From the centre all round to the sea
>   I am lord of the fowl and the brute.
> O Solitude! where are the charms
>   That sages have seen in thy face?
> Better dwell in the midst of alarms
>   Than reign in this horrible place.
>
> .   .   .   .   .
>
> Society, Friendship and Love
>   Divinely bestow'd upon man,
> O had I the wings of a dove
>   How soon would I taste you again!
>   *The Solitude of Alexander Selkirk*—W. Cowper.

But the Creator did not leave Adam to grow tired of solitude. Society, friendship and love were divinely bestowed upon man and in some way, which is now far beyond us to unravel, God provided Adam with a partner—one of his own essential form and nature.

Many have asked how far this simple account is to be taken literally. Perhaps it is not begging that question if we change its form and ask how far the section is to be understood literally—how far it is to be interpreted literally. That the passage, as the writer has set it out in his simple style, is to be taken literally none can doubt. For ordinary readers, for the bulk of mankind, perhaps for all men, it conveys all the truth that man needs to know. He is made from dust, inbreathed with divinely-given life and joined to a partner whose nature is essentially one with his own. But if we now change the form of the question and ask how we are to understand such a mystery the plain answer is that, in any case, no one understands it. Whether we believe implicitly in Genesis or solely in materialistic evolution we do not, and probably cannot, understand it. And so far as the final form of the question is concerned, as to whether or not we should interpret the passage literally, it seems to me we have the choice of two answers. Either, as many of us believe, the story is the true and literal account of the formation of the first two members of the human race, or it is possible that the origin of the race is so extremely complicated, and so far beyond human intelligence to grasp, that it can only be described under some figure of speech and that the Creator has chosen the best possible way of representing what we can never fully understand. In either case we shall come nearest to the truth by taking the story, and interpreting it, literally.

God formed, then, for Adam a partner of his own essential nature. On the purely biological level God had used this pattern for most of His creatures. Reproduction from two sexes gives an immense scope for minor variations within a common pattern. So, as we have said before, the offspring were not to be exact reproductions of the parents in the way that millions of pennies are exact replicas of the master die. Through sexual reproduction the Creator has allowed for an incredible number of variations within the limits of the main pattern. On a higher level, and particularly in the human race, there are the immense advantages of having two parents to look after the offspring and to share the tasks of home. Yet the most profound reason lies clearly on the highest plane of all. We have already seen on several occasions that a materialistic explanation of creation, if taken alone, is incomplete. God made the material world so that it could reflect the spiritual. The same Architect designed both. The same pattern runs through both; the same principles operate in both. The one becomes the type of the other. God gave the first man a bride . . . and every Christian wedding since has been a reminder that this fact is a picture of Christ and His Church (Eph. 5. 32). That love which exists here on earth between husband and wife— the strongest bond in all the world, stronger even than love to father or mother—that bond has been designed by God, not only for man's benefit, but to help him understand the deepest of all spiritual lessons, the love of Christ for His Church. We have reached the ultimate purpose for which the human race was made. For Christ shall not dwell alone without a companion in a solitary eternity, but He will have His bride—those who, even in this life, can sing . . .

> Oh! I am my Beloved's
> And my Beloved's mine!
> He brings a poor vile sinner
> Into His house of wine.
> I stand upon His merit;
> I know no other stand,
> Not e'en where glory dwelleth
> In Immanuel's land.

This, then, is as far, or nearly as far, as we can go. For the questions which lie beyond this point concern the method by which man was created and on this subject the Bible tells us little more than we have discussed above. But many have not been content with that little and have invented theories of their own, and since so many in these days make anxious enquiry concerning the method by which the human race originated, we must turn aside for awhile to consider the subject.

CHAPTER 18

AN ASIDE—CONCERNING THE ORIGIN OF MAN

WE are, in this chapter, raising some questions which are probably among the most difficult and profound known to man. The total number of facts is immense. The number of certain and positive conclusions is very small indeed. The problem has been complicated by two great factors which are frequently overlooked but which lie at the root of nearly all the difficulties. In the first place the discussion is often beclouded by a bitterness of feeling and an intolerance which make it impossible to weigh the evidence fairly. Both on the scientific and on the theological side there is often an appalling—almost wilful—ignorance of the views of the other side. Secondly, the thought-forms and patterns of every age are dominated by certain massive theories which make it very difficult for the people of any age to think independently of the great current theories of that age. This mass psychology is so subtle but powerful that few realise its implication, yet at various times in history it has compelled many to believe in such theories as the rotation of spheres of stars around a fixed earth, or the spontaneous appearance of life, or the view that many chemical processes were due to the gaining or losing of a spirit of phlogiston. Physics in the last century was dominated by the great conceptions of impenetrable and indestructible atoms obeying the laws of Newtonian mathematics, and valuable though these conceptions were they have been compelled to give way to the completely new 'wave mechanical' conception of space and time of our own day. In theology, too, the study of the Bible has been impeded at various stages in history by widely held views such as the allegorizing of all its simple stories by the early church writers, the over-literal interpretation of the zealous writers of the seventeenth century and the wholesale higher critical and modernist views of the last century which reduced the Book to myths and legends. In every case it is possible to find writers using the hackneyed argument 'all scholars are now agreed . . .' and this is regarded as sufficiently massive to crush any opponent . . . and of course to stifle any independent thought. We meet here, too, the full force of what has been called 'Brunner's Law'. [See Emil Brunner, *Christianity and Civilisation*, Gifford Lectures, 1948, Second Part, Lecture IV 'Education']. The further removed a study is from the personal centre of our lives and responsibilities —as for example in Physics and Mathematics—the less will the sinful warping of our nature affect our conclusion. The nearer a study brings us to our personal responsibility to our Creator the more does our sinful nature seek to blind our minds to truths which we do not want to believe and to encourage us to cling to some hypothesis which looks like relieving us of that responsibility.

In view of this, then, it is worth considering that for about a century now human thought has been largely dominated by two massive theories, that of uniformity in geology, by which almost all changes are attributed to the work of gradual forces operating slowly over very long periods, and that of evolution of all forms of life from one original simple form, so that man himself is descended from an ape-like ancestor who was descended from an amoeba-like speck which was descended from neutrons, protons and electrons. It is most difficult indeed to stand outside the current views of one's age, and equally risky to disagree with them! But it is the responsibility of those who seek for truth to make the attempt.

We shall, then, in this chapter seek to state briefly the two extreme opposing views—that of the more literal theologians on the one hand, and that of the confirmed evolutionists on the other. We must then survey the chief facts relevant to the case and try to assess their importance. This should lead us to see how far the two conflicting views need modification and finally to discuss the possibility of a reasonable solution of the problems which seem to arise from the many facts.

Yet I must beg leave once again to underline the fact that this chapter is 'an aside'. Its conclusions are not part of the great progress of the story of creation planned and completed. It is a discussion forced upon us by the theories of evolution, and when this chapter is concluded we can return to the main theme, as we consider the great Sabbath rest of the Creator who could regard all His work as 'very good'.

1. *The literal, orthodox theological view.*

This view is put forward perhaps most clearly in that master-piece of logic and literature, P. H. Gosse's *Omphalos*, which suggests that the entire human race is descended from two parents, Adam and Eve, the former of whom (Adam) was created fully grown and as a perfect specimen of humanity on a day which, if Ussher's chronology of the Old Testament is accepted, fell in the year 4004 B.C.[1] Being of perfect human stature, like any other living creature he, Adam, must needs have had in his body evidences of a previous history, which evidences would, however, be completely false. Just as a tree, if created fully grown, would contain rings indicating scientifically an age of many years— which it never had—just as an elephant, if created fully grown, would show molars which indicated twenty or thirty years of growth—'prochronic' evidence which must needs be false—so Adam, if created fully grown, would have a navel (Greek Omphalos) indicating scientifically a parent which in fact he never had. With inexorable logic Gosse pursues his point through every region of nature, from the lowest form of life to the highest, and shows that we are no better off if we start with a seed or a babe.[2] The scientific evidence of an earlier stage is inevitably present. It is the old 'hen and egg' problem put in its most rigid and scientific form. Gosse has been laughed at and neglected, and his general conclusion I think rightly rejected, but in scientific knowledge, clearness of logic and humility he stands out far above many of his critics who have failed to grasp the implication of his arguments or who have never even read his original work. We may not, however, at this stage pause to consider in detail the force of Gosse's particular theory of 'prochronism' though we shall meet it again, but must continue with a summary of the orthodox theological view of man's origin. This maintains that all human skulls must be dated as post-Adamic and that unusual forms like those of Neandertal man would represent some early branch of the Adamic race that became extinct in the early stone age.

As evidence for this view we have, on the theological side, the

---

[1] See, however, p. 150.

[2] Even one of Prof. Hoyle's spontaneously created protons travelling along some path in space would provide 'prochronic' evidence that a few years before it was some millions of miles further away—when in fact it did not exist.

obvious fact that it arises most simply from the text of Genesis
1-2 and from the consistent use by the Hebrews of the word *Adam*
for the human race. It is borne out, too, by the New Testament
writers who base their argument on the oneness of the race as
seen in its head, Adam, the *one* man who sinned, just as forgiveness
comes through the *one* man, Christ, the head of the new creation.

The literal view is also supported by the very simple common-
sense argument that as we can frequently trace very large families
back to two great grandparents so logically it is easy to believe
that the human race would go back ultimately to two ancestors.
It is further supported by the common observations, into which
we shall enquire more diligently later, on the present unity of the
race. Man is obviously a single species capable of intermarriage
and, within correctly chosen groups, inter-blood donation. His
complex chemical hormones are of the same formula, his number
of chromosomes is constant throughout. He is of size and weight
and longevity governed by a gaussian distribution about a mean
value. He is mainly right-handed and, although he speaks many
languages, one from any tribe can learn, and ultimately speak, the
language of any other. The fundamental inner nature of all men
seems to be the same, and wherever men of any race have accepted
the Christian gospel they have forthwith recognized all other such
as their brothers, with a common stock of hopes and fears and
feelings and forms of thought.

2. *The scientific theory.*

The purely scientific theory is more difficult to formulate as its
exponents, while agreeing that the theological view just outlined
must be rejected completely, do not themselves altogether agree
upon the method by which man came into being.[1] Yet they have
much in common and this we can seek to outline.

It is generally believed that some hundred million years or so
ago, a group of creatures called tarsioids begat descendants which
underwent gradual modifications along several branching lines one

---

[1] 'Although there is complete agreement among professional students that
man is a member of that order of mammals to which Linnaeus gave the name
"Primates" and that his lineage when traced backwards, will be found to branch
off from the primate tree, there is a sharp difference of opinion as to the exact
point in the tree and the approximate date in geological time, at which the
human branch separates from those other main branches which represent the
lineage of anthropoid apes and of monkeys.'—Sir Arthur Keith in article MAN,
Enc. Brit. XIVth Ed., 1929.

of which led to the gibbons and another to the anthropoids of the Miocene period. These latter in turn produced descendants whose modifications were sufficient to divide them into at least four groups: chimpanzees, gorillas, orangs, and a group which yet again subdivided into 'near-man', Neandertal man and modern man, Homo sapiens. It is further generally agreed that the time-scale for modern man must be extended by several thousand years, and that for 'early man' by a matter of some hundreds of thousands of years.

The evidences for this view can be found set out in books on Biology or on Evolution and normally follow some such lines as the following:

(a) Man's body shows a remarkable similarity in pattern to that of the gorilla, orang or chimpanzee.
(b) In man's embryonic development there seem to be traces of the repeating (recapitulation) of the early stages of evolutionary development.
(c) Man possesses a number of anatomical curiosities which seem to be relics, vestigial remains, of an earlier stage of development.
(d) The study of slightly changing modern forms, and also of successive fossil forms, of various creatures indicates the possibility of a kind of radiating development although usually of definite trend and limited scope. Analogy would suggest that man arose by some such process.
(e) The study of fossil remains and the work of archaeologists have produced a number of ancient skulls, bones and tools which seem to demand an antiquity of many tens of thousands of years and to presuppose more than one pair of ancestors.

The next task before us is to attempt a brief survey of the chief facts or factors involved and to assess their relevance to the two major views outlined above and then to consider how far these facts necessitate some modifications of the more extreme views.

1. *The Unity of the human race.*
There can be no conceivable doubt that the present human race is a homogeneous unit. There are no beings alive anywhere on this earth today about whom any real doubt can possibly be entertained. The most remote and primitive tribe—shall we say the Auca Indians—may still be in the early stone age and may murder Christian missionaries . . . but the missionaries who willingly gave their lives, and the noble wives who deliberately

followed up their work, were right in concluding that the Auca Indians are at heart truly lovable human brothers and sisters. The Auca 'George' was as truly a man as George Washington or George VI although the gulf in mentality and character was so vast. Members of every race and tribe are capable of intermarrying and indeed have done so. Man shows an ability to make and use tools which places him in a class apart. This ability, like so many of his gifts, is distributed over a wide range so that it is possible to point to a number of unfortunate individuals with little innate ability. But care must be taken to allow also for lack of opportunity. It is well known that it is possible to bring individuals from so-called primitive tribes and train them in modern colleges to become doctors or architects or engineers of no mean ability. Dr. Barnardo did the same for some of the poorest and most degraded of waifs from the London slums. It is true that at the lower end of the scale there are necessarily some of our brethren who will never 'make the grade' and it is true that some chimpanzees can be trained to do trick motor-cycle rides, etc., in circuses . . . but the great gap is still there. No group of apes has yet made its own bows and arrows or boomerangs or drawn pictures of itself on cave walls, to say nothing of making books, machines or engines. It is futile to maintain that there is at present any misty zone between the anthropoid apes and man. It is better to face in full the whole weight of the argument that mentally between the mean of the apes' intelligence and the mean of human intelligence there is an incredible gulf. This gulf because it is different in kind as well as degree is vaster than that between the ape and the amoeba. The present human race considered from the point of view of body, mind or spirit, is a homogeneous unit and is unique. So vast and staggering is the gulf between man and the apes, particularly in the realm of intelligence, that even so great a champion of evolution as Sir Julian Huxley admits that the great 'jump' could have taken place only once and that it would probably never take place again.[1] In other words he admits that man was a special creation.

---

[1]'Only along one single line is progress and its future possibility being continued—the line of man. If man were wiped out it is in the highest degree improbable that the step to conceptual thought would again be taken even by his nearest kin. After 1500 million years of evolution progress hangs on but a single thread. That thread is the human germ-plasm.'—Julian Huxley, M.A., D.Sc., F.R.S., *Evolution: the Modern Synthesis*. (C. Allen & Unwin, 1942).

If it be argued that as we go back in history we shall find in time what we cannot find in space then we must first of all distinguish clearly between true intelligence and accumulated knowledge. When this is done we are faced with the fact that for thousands of years human intelligence does not seem to have changed. The intelligence of the average Babylonian of 500 B.C. seems to have differed little from the average of the present inhabitants of Baghdad. The Greeks of Athens in the days of Aristotle differed little in fundamental intelligence from the present inhabitants of Oxford or Edinburgh. At the higher end of the scale we note that the world's great geniuses are not crowded into the last fifty years. In the formulation of legal codes Hammurabi (or some of his predecessors), as well as Moses and Solon and Justinian and Alfred the Great have all played their part. Modern times can claim no monopoly of literary geniuses: Scott and Dickens and Tolstoy and Tennyson must share their honours with Goethe and Dante, Shakespeare and Milton, Euripedes and Aristophanes, Hesiod and Homer. Some of our modern artists could doubtless hold their own with the cave painters of Dordogne but for genius in art we must still go back to Rubens and van Dyke, to Michelangelo and Phidias. We cannot easily overlook the intelligence that lay behind the design and building of the greater pyramids of Egypt whose massive blocks were cut with amazing accuracy and whose base angles are true to within a small fraction of a degree. We may not know who designed the Parthenon but he would have been a worthy companion for Wren. Solomon and Hezekiah who designed the water supplies of Jerusalem and the Roman engineers who built the vast aqueducts in Spain might easily have shared the same lectures as those attended by Brunel or Telford or the builders of the Aswan dam. The progress of physics and chemistry rests not only on the work of the modern geniuses, Einstein, Planck, Rutherford, Curie and the like but also on the patient work and profound observations of the earlier thinkers—of Galileo and Newton, Scheele and Cavendish, Davy and Faraday to name but a few. It is even probable that biology and geology would have made greater progress if they could have broken free from a mysterious over-reverence for the views of two men from a single period, Darwin and Lyell, and could have been willing to reconsider some of the contributions of earlier experts in those fields or to explore some new theories in a new age. Certainly in mathematics the great names are scattered through the centuries, Euclid, Pythagoras, Ptolemy, Descartes, Leibnitz, Newton, Pascal, Bessel, Riemann. Among philosophers and theologians we should find it hard today to place any modern thinkers alongside Plato, Aristotle, Origen, Augustine, Francis Bacon or Calvin. We may have seen in two world wars some great generals. They must share the field with Napoleon, Wellington, Marlborough, Edward I, Julius Caesar, Hannibal, Alexander and possibly Tuthmosis III.

So we might go on, but the conclusion is clear enough. So far as historical evidence goes there is no evidence that there has been any increase in man's innate intelligence since he began to write.

Today there is no trace of evidence among the world's 2,600 million inhabitants of any doubtful creatures intermediate between true man and creatures of some anthropoid stock. Going back over that range of history since man first left any records in writing, drawing or building, the story is the same. Such a survey covers a host of far more than ten thousand million beings all of whom were truly human. Against such a background—usually ignored or explained away—it is well to pause before constructing some hypothetical scheme which rests upon the uncertain interpretation of some dozens of skulls—or fragments—among which are one or two more difficult to account for than the rest.

2. *The similarity of pattern between man and the higher animals.*

We must next consider the very obvious fact that running through the structures of many creatures there is an evident similarity of pattern. Whole groups of creatures, for example, have a backbone and it might be inferred that they were therefore all descended from a few creatures who first developed the rudiments of such a structure. Many creatures have a 'five-fingered hand' although it may be so modified as to become a wing or a fin. The common pattern might reasonably be used as one piece of evidence that in some cases more complex forms have arisen by descent with modification from simpler forms. As we have already noted Genesis 1, in its highly condensed account, makes no attempt to describe 'how' the earth 'brought forth' the various creatures which now adorn it. The Christian only asserts that whatever happened was not in the ultimate sense a random development but that it was planned. In the Biblical language it was done as God said it should be done.

But does similarity of pattern always and necessarily require common descent? Plainly, no. It is merely the outward evidence of a vast generalization that we might even call a law . . . the law of Comparable Effect. Whenever similar forces act in similar circumstances the results will be similar. As many of God's creatures must live in fairly similar circumstances and as these creatures are produced by similar forces, light, heat, electrical and chemical energy operating on the same types of atoms, the products will be somewhat similar. The pattern is the best for the whole set of circumstances. The law of comparable effects is probably one of the widest 'laws' of the universe. We find stars in one galaxy of similar pattern to those in another. We conclude that similar forces are operating in similar circumstances. We find that magnesium oxide has a crystal structure similar to that of rock salt. We conclude that similar forces have acted on somewhat similar atoms, but it would be absurd to conclude that one had ever 'come from' the other. The deadly poison, carbon monoxide, has many of its physical properties almost identical with those of the harmless nitrogen. We know now that very similar forces acting around similar atoms have in this case produced almost identical 'electron' patterns. There are, in fact, millions of examples in the universe of similarity of pattern; they do not prove common descent, but merely the action of similar forces in similar circumstances. If the Creator chooses to design a number of different creatures to live in similar yet slightly differing circumstances, and if He chooses to limit Himself to the use of a certain number of types of energy acting on and through a limited number of types of atoms, it follows that the creatures produced will manifest many similarities. Whether they are descended from one another is an entirely separate question which must be proved by other means. Similarity of structure itself is no proof of common descent.

If we may approach the same question from another angle we might observe that man himself uses a small number of general, simple principles and modifies them to suit slightly differing purposes. Thus the lever, the wheel, the pulley and the screw are used in hundreds of slightly different forms in hundreds of different machines . . . evidence of a common designer (man) working conformably with the law of comparable effects. The similarity of pattern observed in many groups of creatures is, then, a strong evidence of a single Designer working to the maximum efficiency within certain limitations of energy and matter. By itself it constitutes no proof of genetic relationship. Man, in order to fulfil his part in the purpose and plan of the Creator, could only have been built as he was. Had he differed fundamentally from other creatures which are themselves ideally fitted to live in a very similar environment he himself would obviously not have been best suited to his surroundings. In other words God's work would not have been 'very good'.

When we consider that beyond the similarity of general structure there are also the innumerable minor variations of pattern each of which fits man better for his environment and destiny, we have overwhelming evidence of the work of one supreme Designer varying His pattern to suit varying needs; and all of this together constitutes in itself no evidence for or against organic relationship. So far as all this evidence goes the Creator might have worked through organic descent with gradual modifications, or He might have introduced new types of creatures by some more rapid means. A final consideration of the similarity of pattern together with the incredible number of minor, positively useful variations, can never of itself be used as proof of the organic descent of man from the higher primates. The similarities and the differences would have been there in any case.

3. *The 'Recapitulation' Theory*

Living things start from a single tiny fertilized cell which divides, grows, divides and grows, and by the constant repetition of this scheme becomes an ever-increasingly complicated structure more and more completely fitted to the tasks for which it is ultimately intended. It follows that while the lines of this development are leading ever further apart for creatures that will ultimately differ, they must be very much closer together during the earlier stages. The observation that in the early stages of development all animals are very much alike was made by Karl Ernst von Baer (1792-1876) in 1824-1828, but he certainly was not the originator of that perversion of his views which arose some years later, and, in fact, he was never able fully to accept Darwin's theory of unbroken descent with modifications.

Robert Chambers in *Vestiges of the Natural History of Creation* —a book which appeared anonymously in 1844—suggested that not only other creatures but man himself in his embryonic development went through stages resembling those of lowlier forms, namely, 'fish, a reptile, a bird and the lowest mammalia before attaining specific maturity'. He asserts that at one stage the human embryo is ape-like. The idea, which Chambers calls a law, was seized upon with unfortunate zeal by Ernst Haeckel (1834-1919) who repeated and stressed it as a fundamental 'biogenetic law' of recapitulation,[1] that an organism passes through an epitome of the modifications undergone by its ancestors in the course of their evolution. Haeckel's enthusiasm for the theory, which he supported with some falsified evidence, led to some useful research into the embryonic development of various creatures, but to no useful evidence for their evolutionary line of ascent. The theory is, in fact, now admitted by almost all to be a gross exaggeration or, more likely, completely false. If true it would require a theory of evolution which is not acceptable to evolutionists. It would require that evolution had taken place by the constant addition of new stages at the *end* of the development of the previous stages. This theory of hypermorphism[2] is not conformable to, or accepted by, the modern theory which demands that modifications have occurred in all stages and not only in the last stage of each development that led to new creatures.

We might therefore have happily dismissed the recapitulation theory as being just another example of a man's failure to interpret correctly the operation of the law of comparable effects, and as a hypothesis now repudiated even by the strongest advocates of the evolutionary theory. But error dies hard and we are constantly confronted with two little bits of the rejected theory—namely the oft-repeated statements that man must be descended from some monkey-like[3] ancestor, and more remotely from fishes, because the human embryo has a tail and gills. These crude mis-statements have survived long after the parent theory has been disowned and it is too often forgotten that, since the main theory of recapitulation is now rejected, these two misrepresentations, which are part of it, are in any case of no value.

But it is a complete misuse of words to say that the human embryo has a tail in the sense that that word is used in ordinary

---

[1] That ontogeny recapitulates phylogeny.
[2] G. S. Carter, *Animal Evolution*, p. 322-3.
[3] Not ape—for apes have no tails.

English and applied to a dog or cat. During the development of the embryos of those creatures which are to have a backbone it is found that the spine is clearly formed quite early and the body is progressively developed along it from the head end. This means that the 20- or 30-day embryos, which are of course extremely tiny, give the appearance that the last part of the spine is left as a tail. At this stage the legs are present only as two tiny buds. By 40 days there are traces of toes and it is quite clear that the last vertebrae will never be a tail, and when the process of formation of all the main features is complete at about 60 days the tiny embryo, now an inch long, shows no trace whatever of a tail. The spine, then, of the human embryo is never any longer than is required for the complete development of a tail-less being. To say that the human embryo has a tail, in the same sense as one speaks of a dog or monkey having a tail, is completely misleading and untrue. It is a real disservice to the more scientific discussion of the evidence for evolution that such crude and suspect means should ever have been tolerated.

The statement that 'it is plain that we came from fishes because the human embryo has gills', is just as misleading and untrue. Water is able to dissolve some oxygen from the air, more, in fact, in proportion than it does nitrogen. Fishes require oxygen and by the simple process of taking water into their mouths and expelling it through the gill slits they are able in an extremely short space of time to extract as much oxygen as they require. The developing human embryo also requires oxygen and the tiny little structure, less than an inch long, early develops a very simple heart, and the artery from this forms an arch supplying the upper part of the body and bending round to supply the middle and lower regions. More such arteries are formed close together with furrows between them. In fishes these develop into gill slits. In the human embryo they follow a completely different path giving rise to parts of the neck and face. They are never open; they are never clefts or slits. The human embryo never has gill slits like those of a fish. Like all tiny embryos it has that system of blood vessels best suited to its immediate environment and its future development. It has nothing to do with the structure of its alleged ancestors millions of years ago. Every vertebrate creature besides man shows this type of development but each works the scheme out differently to its own particular pattern and need. We conclude, then, that the factors controlling the development of the human embryo are not some condensed residual memories of bygone ancestors, but are the actual physical and chemical forces which, operating within a perfectly co-ordinated plan, best fit the tiny growing organism to its immediate but highly complex environment and finally develop it into that marvel of intricate design which we call the living human infant. The human babe is a million times stronger proof of a Great Designer than it is of a recapitulation theory or random development hypothesis.

The question of vestigial remains is closely allied to the story of recapitulation. It is most commonly considered in the cases of animals further down the scale than the primates but it has sometimes been put forward as providing evidence that man has evolved from a more primitive ancestor, though it is by no means clear to which ancestor the evidence is supposed to point. These vestigial or unwanted remains fall into two classes, namely those which seem to be of no use to any human being and those which seem to be of no use to the members of one sex. Such things as the coccyx, the vermiform appendix, the little fold in the corner of the eye, and even the wisdom teeth have been quoted in the former group. The coccyx is important for the attachment of several muscles, and incidentally is not getting shorter for it is just the same in some of the most ancient skeletons. The appendix appears to be responsible for secretions which promote movement of the intestines to assist digestion, although its functions can be taken over by other organs so that it is not missed when removed. The little fold in the corner of the eye is useful for the removing of tiny specks of dust. So far as wisdom teeth are concerned it is difficult to see how the fact that some people have jaws which are a little too small, to permit of these, can be used as evidence that they have evolved a little further than folk with wisdom teeth. Does natural selection favour the happy folk who have no wisdom teeth?

To the second group belong a few factors such as the well-known fact that male human beings possess unused mammae on their chests. Darwin seems seriously to have supposed that this was because human beings had descended from some creatures where the males assisted in suckling the young. Surely a better sense of humour would have saved him from such a suggestion! Evidently it was a step forward in evolutionary progress when the males gave up the job. Seriously, however, it is of course only part of a much wider fact that the fertilized egg contains all the genes that control the development of all the male and female organs. The sex chromosome working through complex chemical substances determines which shall become functional and which shall not, so that in the case quoted the mammae never really develop in the male. The evidence points once again to an extremely wonderful pattern or plan which is being worked out even in the case of some apparently unwanted parts of the body.

We come next to a study that is obviously of much greater importance and extent. There have been found many ancient skulls and skeletons, and many ancient implements evidently made by early man, and it is confidently asserted by some that man was emerging from the condition of a brute some 500,000 years ago. It is alleged that it took him many tens of thousands of years to make even a slight improvement in his flint tools and that it is possible, by noting these often relatively slight differences, to be assured that some were made nearly half a million years before others. Half a *million*! The position obviously calls for some investigation. There seems little doubt that in many areas human beings have followed a sequence in the materials they have used: stone, copper, bronze, iron. With a little care historical and pre-historical times can be mapped out by a kind of sequence-dating:

Flint using	Old Stone Age	Palaeolithic
	Middle ,, ,,	Mesolithic
	New ,, ,,	Neolithic
Copper using		Chalcolithic
Bronze ,,		Bronze Age
Iron ,,		Iron Age

It is at once obvious that the term 'age', especially as applied to the world as a whole, or even to any large area, is most misleading. There are a few regions in S. America, C. Africa and C. Asia which are still in their Bronze Age and a few in S. America and Australia in their Stone Age. It is not always safe, even in one area, to assume that the sequence can be accurately dated. The Stone Age Auca Indians of Equador live quite near to regions where 500 years *earlier* the highly civilized Incas used copper and gold. Further if, as some assert, techniques and styles of flint-chipping spread extremely slowly from one land to another, then in the nature of the case similar tools in different lands are by no means necessarily contemporary.

When we come to the question of absolute rather than relative dating for ancient objects we run into certain difficulties. There are two main methods available. These are (a) the radio-carbon method (b) the archaeological-geological method.

(a) *The radio-carbon method.*

This extremely interesting method depends upon the fact that the carbon dioxide of the air contains a very small amount of radio-carbon often called carbon-14 as its atoms are a little heavier than those of ordinary carbon which are rated at 12. So far as can be ascertained the percentage of ^{14}C is constant all over the world and its presence seems to be due to cosmic ray activity. Although the cosmic ray activity varies over different parts of the world the proportion of ^{14}C in the atmosphere seems constant, a fact which must be due to efficient stirring by winds and other means. The only point here open to question is whether the cosmic ray activity has been sufficiently constant over the whole period under review. There is some indirect evidence that it might have been approximately so[1] but there is also some evidence that changes have occurred in the past.

Now all living material derives its carbon ultimately from the carbon dioxide of the atmosphere and hence shows the same percentage of ^{14}C. Any specimen of wood which shows the full amount of radio-activity must be modern. As soon as a living thing dies it ceases to take in any more ^{14}C. Its own ^{14}C breaks up by radio-active decay at a speed which seems to be governed, like all radio-activity, by an inexorable law of logarithmic rate of decay. The radio-activity will fall to one-half of its original value in about 5,760 years, to a quarter in 11,520 years and to one eighth in 17,280 years.

It is quite simple to draw a graph for this rate of decay or to substitute figures for it in a logarithmic formula and hence, if the radio-active intensity of any sample can be accurately measured, the date can at once be read. The exact value for the half-life is still open to a small margin of disagreement and the exact determination of radio-active intensity of a given specimen requires very careful recording owing to the 'background' effects of cosmic ray activity. These difficulties are gradually being reduced and

---

[1] Radio carbon dating. W. F. Libby. *Proc. Chem. Soc.*, May 1960, p. 166.

the only real trace of uncertainty lies in the assumption that the percentage of ^{14}C in the air has been constant since Palaeolithic times.

Wood from ancient tombs and from the heart of giant sequoia trees, whose annual rings could be counted, has been tested and gives dates fairly close to those which could be checked by ordinary means or historical data. Linen from the pots in which the Dead Sea scrolls were stored gave an age of 1917±200 years while wood from tombs of early Pharaohs gave ages of 4,000 to 5,000 years, i.e. 2,000 to 3,000 B.C. Charcoal from Stonehenge indicated a date around 1600 B.C. but some grains of wheat from early Egyptian granaries indicated 4,300 B.C. which seems somewhat too high. Very early remains of human activity usually give dates around 10,000 years ago (8,000 B.C.) although charcoal from the Lascaux cave in France reached 13,000 B.C. Incidentally it becomes much more difficult to count true radio-active intensity free from 'background' at much beyond 15,000 years (three half lives) and the Lascaux figure probably has a wide margin of error. Radio-carbon methods used on charcoal at Jericho seem to indicate that the site was occupied by very early (pre-pottery) neolithic man at about 7,000 B.C.

If, then, subsequent research enables us to be sure of the constancy of the proportion of ^{14}C in the atmosphere up to 20,000 years we can say that the radio-carbon method indicates a date of up to 7,000 B.C. for the Neolithic period and around 13,000 B.C. for the Palaeolithic man of the Lascaux cave age.[1]

(b) *Geological methods.*

These methods attempt to correlate the dates of very early specimens with certain geological features, namely those attributed to four stages of the ice ages. These four stages are named after four tributaries of the Danube and are assigned dates which are based on an astronomical theory of the ice age and of a climatic optimum which followed the last of the four. These four ice-age periods, with suggested dates, are:

1. Gunz	590,000—550,000 B.C.	
2. Mindel	476,000—435,000 B.C.	
3. Riss	230,000—187,000 B.C.	
4. Wurm	115,000— 25,000 B.C.	

---

[1] Recent discoveries seem to indicate that the radio-carbon content of the atmosphere was less in early days and hence these dates will have to be considerably reduced. (1965).

The periods between these are called interglacial. It is believed that after the last the climate improved to give a 'climatic optimum' dated 8,000 to 3,000 years ago, i.e. 6,000 B.C. to 1,000 B.C. It will be seen that the dates are extremely vague and it must be remembered that they are based on one single theory of ice-ages and glacial retreat that is by no means universally accepted. Moreover, as at present the world's glaciers have shown considerable retreat in the last hundred years, it is hardly likely that the changes were so incredibly slow in the past. However these 'astronomical' dates are at present extremely popular with those who seek to date Palaeolithic remains, although they require periods like a hundred thousand years for the human race to make a tiny improvement in stone implements. It is also necessary to believe that some 17 feet of debris in the Pin Hole cave in Derbyshire represent over 100,000 years whereas such would normally mean 1,000 to 2,000 years unless vast periods occurred when the cave was unoccupied.

A considerable amount of evidence has been accumulating for some time that the 'astronomical' chronology is far too high. Some of this evidence is given by Velikowsky in his book *Earth in Upheaval*, where he gives studies of the immense deposits of bones in Alaska and in the 'Ivory' islands as well as in Siberia and China. There are also interesting studies of the Siwalik Hills, the Himalayas, the Andes, Arabia and finally of some of the glaciers. He shows, as others have done before, that Lyell's estimate of 35,000 years for the recession of Niagara Falls would be better if reduced to between 2,000 and 5,000 years! The evidence throughout is that the astronomical dates are vastly too high but, perhaps unfortunately, Mr. Velikowsky obscures the value of his arguments by introducing some theories of his own respecting ancient times, and views which at present seem unlikely to command acceptance. Sober studies of archaeological remains, however, do show that most of the stages of human development have occupied only a matter of centuries or at most a thousand or so years each and even if we allow 2,000 years for the Neolithic period, another 1,000 for the Mesolithic and as many as 5,000 for the Palaeolithic we should only arrive at 10,000 B.C. . . . and not at 590,000!

Apart from the problems of absolute dating we have the question of the character and nature of the men whose skulls and skeletons have been unearthed. These skeletons show some variations from one another and some differ from those of modern man. The variations do not seem very important although popular writers and artists, drawing mainly on imagination, have produced wonderful descriptions and illustrations of these early beings.

Some of the skeletons are very incomplete . . . mere fragments . . . and deductions drawn from them are of little value. Others do not show much of importance. The jaw and teeth of a creature called Proconsul africanus only show that the creature was an ape even if, as Dr. Leakey claims, it is just a little more like that of a man than usual. The many skeletons of 'Dryopithecus' found from Spain to the Siwalik hills all belonged to apes. Not one was human at all. So, too, fragments rejoicing in names like Australopithecus, Paranthropus and Plesianthropus are only fragments of apes which possibly had one or two features a little more like the human than usual. At present so little is known for certain about the finds of Dr. Eugene Dubois (1891-8) that his so-called Pithecanthropus erectus is best left for the experts themselves to resolve. If the thigh bone really belonged to the same creature which owned the skull cap then he walked (as the name suggests) erect and it gives no evidence for the poor slouching ape-man of the popular—but purely imaginary—illustrations. Nor do the experts agree about the fragments of some 40 skulls of the so-called 'Pekin' man. Some assert that he was identical with the Java man (Pithecanthropus) while others say the difference is subgeneric! We can afford to wait for something a little more definite. A few very large, ancient teeth have been discovered in 'medicine shops' in China and, as von Koenigswald and Dr. Weidenreich point out, if the owners of these were men they must have been giants. But then, of course, Genesis 6 says so as well.

A large number of skeletons and fragments have been found, representing members of an Old Stone age race generally called Neandertal men. The earliest of these was found at Gibraltar in 1848 and the next—which gave the name to the group—in 1856 in a cave in the valley (thal) of the Neander, near Dusseldorf. Two almost complete skeletons were found at Spy (Belgium) in 1886 and many fragments at Krapina in Croatia in 1899. A solitary jaw found at Heidelberg in 1907 probably belonged to a man of the same type. Many others of the Neandertal type have been found in Western Europe, including Britain, Eastern Europe, Palestine and even as far as Tashkent and China. The majority show receding foreheads and chins[1] and large brow ridges. Yet some of the more eastern specimens have quite steep foreheads and definite chins. They seem on the whole to have been a short race, heavily built but with a brain capacity of about 1450 cc. quite comparable with that of modern man. The brow ridges are due to some minute variation in the chemical make-up of one of the hormones of the body, and it is not quite safe to say that they disappeared with the Old Stone Age. The skull of 'Rhodesia man' (1300 cc.) found at Broken Hill, N. Rhodesia, in 1921, has huge brow ridges but was associated with remains of living, modern species of animals.

Yet another race of early men made their way into Western Europe possibly coming, as did the Moors in historical times, along the coast of North Africa and migrating into France and Western Europe. Typical skeletons of these were found in a rock shelter, Cro-Magnon, near the village of Les Eyzies, Dordogne, France, and hence the race has been called Cro-Magnon man. Many skulls and skeletons of this race are known. One group showed an average height of just under 6 feet with brain capacity slightly exceeding that of modern man. They had, however, marked brow ridges. They were able to produce very neat stone tools and also worked bone and ivory. They made sculptures and artistic engravings, and cave paintings using simple pigments. They used red ochre in their funeral rites. They were hunters, capable of riding horses and making bows and arrows, and they were alive when the mammoth still existed. They had reached the zenith of civilization of an old world when suddenly they and their civilization . . . and the mammoths . . . disappeared from the records.

The next comers, the so-called Mesolithic men, had lost the art of their fathers (if fathers they were) and could produce only rough flints and crude implements with poor decorations. But human inventiveness soon reasserted itself and within a few centuries new cultures appeared in relatively quick succession taking us into the Neolithic or New Stone Age. Instruments were well-polished, agriculture and weaving were developed

---

[1] There is a curious statement in ancient Jewish tradition (see Rev. J. Hellmuth, *Biblical Thesaurus*, Genesis, p. 67) that in the days of Enosh men's faces assumed ape-like form and features.

and soon the first traces of the use of metal appeared. These were the times of the 'standing stones', of Carnac and of Stonehenge, and we have reached a relatively fixed dating around 1500 to 2000 B.C. In various parts of the world this age merges straight into the Early Bronze Age and to times which, because of the first written records, we call historical.

The scientific facts are, then, on the whole reasonably straightforward and certainly nowhere startling. From the purely scientific point of view the only points which seem doubtful are the 'astronomical' dates for Palaeolithic man.

We have now to consider the question 'How far do these facts run parallel to the Biblical account'? Here it seems to me that at present we lack sufficient data to give a single definite answer. There are three possible solutions to the problem that confront us. One of these maintains that the name Adam does not refer to a single individual but to a race. The other two views accept the statement that Adam was a single individual.

1. The first explanation, to which allusion has already been made earlier, is that the 'Adam and Eve' of Genesis 2 are symbolic or literary figures, the story of whose fall is meant to convey a real and true spiritual fact about the nature of man but one which is too profound for any straightforward account. It could be regarded as a divinely given parable, superior to legends or myths of mere human invention, and would allow scope for any chronology, long or short, and for any number of various types of skulls. It is argued that if the story of creation in Chapter 1 is set in a literary form then so is the account of the fall in Chapter 2. But it may well be answered that there is a vast difference. We can never understand how God created matter and light, and the beginnings of life are far too complex for any other form of description than that of Genesis 1. But we can quite easily understand human beings being faced with a choice and making the wrong choice. We do it ourselves. It requires no parable; the fact is not too difficult for anyone to grasp.

This first explanation is more in favour among the 'liberal' theologians but less among the more cautious. It is more difficult to reconcile with the New Testament doctrines, especially those of Romans 5. 12-21 and 1 Corinthians 15. 21-22 where the one man Adam is plainly contrasted with the one Man Christ Jesus. Even so, this explanation of Genesis 2 is accepted by such cautious and reverent students as Drs. Sanday and Headlam in their excellent commentary on Romans, where they do not find that it causes them insuperable difficulties.

If, on the other hand, we accept the position that the Biblical Adam and Eve were two real persons we have two possible lines of exegesis turning upon the question as to whether or not we allow the existence of pre-Adamic or co-Adamic 'men'. We shall, then, consider the known facts about early man in the light of these two possibilities.

2. The theory that a pre-Adamic race existed.

We have already considered the question of the unity of the present human race. The view under consideration maintains that the present race is descended from two ancestors—Adam and Eve—who were specially endowed by God with a spiritual nature and were placed in an ideal environment in which, however, they failed to obey the word of the Creator. But in the further world around them—beyond this 'garden land'—there dwelt, or had dwelt maybe long before, other beings similar in structure though not identical, and devoid of that inner spiritual nature which constituted true 'man' i.e. Adam. These beings might be identified with the Old Stone Age men, or with even earlier forms. Either they died out before Adam or maybe their descendants continued until the time of the Flood. None now remains. Adam's date, on such a view, could be Mesolithic or Neolithic or somewhere among the Palaeolithic times. On the Scofield Bible hypothosis these pre-Adamic, Palaeolithic men might have lived away back in the 'gap period'. Some have even held that Satan, before his own fall, was overlord of this race. It must be recognized that such theories are far more highly speculative than the views of most scientists and come strangely from those who constantly denounce science as based on conjecture while they themselves demand explanations based on facts.

But we may not reject a possible theory because some carry it too far. Let us weigh the evidences for a pre-Adamic race. On the scientific side it seems to have no objection except, perhaps, that anatomically Neandertal men seem so like modern men in almost all respects that one hesitates to make them a separate race. Again their artistic ability, and possible spiritual outlook as suggested by burial customs, strongly point to identity with modern men. Yet scientifically it might be possible to defend a theory that

Homo sapiens is a mutation from a man-like stock and is to be equated with the Biblical 'descendant of Adam', while the earlier stock—now extinct—never attained to the dignity of Homo sapiens or Adamic.

On the theological side it seems necessary to support this theory by a second hypothesis, namely that the pre-Adamic race died out completely, as the Bible seems to insist clearly that all men are now Adamic.

The theologian will, however, ask for positive evidence from the Bible and here there is a little which may be worth examining. Some seven points have been put forward.

(1) In Genesis 1. 28 God commanded man to multiply and 'replenish' the earth. This has been used to argue that it must therefore have been previously occupied by an earlier race. Although the R.V. keeps 'replenish' it seems difficult to justify a translation different from that in verse 22 where the word is translated 'fill', and hence it is not safe to build much on this verse.

(2) In Genesis 1. 27 and 5. 2 it is said that God created *them*, and hence it is argued that others beside Adam are included. It must be noted first that the word cannot apply to pre-Adamic man, for v. 27 says 'God created man (Adam) . . .' and hence the word must refer to Adamic, or at least, though less likely, co-Adamic man, and not to pre-Adamic. These verses cannot, then, be used to support a theory of a pre-Adamic race.

(3) Since the account in Genesis 2 shows that Adam could speak it is argued that he must belong to a late period in the development of a race which had gradually acquired that art.

The origin of language is too vast a question to discuss here but it is pure hypothesis, devoid of support, to assert that man very slowly developed the ability to speak. It is quite reasonable to believe that the Creator endowed man with the power of speech when He breathed into him the breath of life.[1] In New Testament times and later it is not unknown for human beings to speak in something akin to a new language either under the influence of the Holy Spirit or of extreme ecstasy.

---

[1] Here we meet the full weight of Gosse's argument as set out in his book Omphalos. The evidence that Adam had to learn little by little how to speak would be 'prochronic'—but false—evidence.

(4) It has been pointed out that since Abel was a shepherd and Cain an agriculturalist the setting of the story must be late Neolithic and certainly not early Palaeolithic. The evidence is of some weight but is not conclusive. The account puts Adam and his family in some very fertile part of the earth, far removed from the conditions of the cave dwellers of France or Germany in times when the whole climatic set-up of the earth had already begun to change. A small, primitive, local 'civilization' of Adam and his family might easily have existed around Eden. There are still some wandering tribes which have not reached settled agricultural life, but it would not be safe to date them 10,000 years earlier than neighbouring tribes who have thus progressed. It is possible that for a time some of Adam's descendants who wandered far across the world had lost the agricultural and pastoral skills.

(5) Cain went out from God's presence and married a wife and built a city which he called 'Enoch'. This must surely have occurred when the region was already populated. Here again the weight of the argument cannot altogether be ignored but it is inconclusive. If the human race sprang from one pair alone then 'brother-sister' marriage is inevitable. There has never been any difficulty here. A number of the Pharaohs, not only of early times like those of the eighteenth dynasty, but also among the Ptolemies, married their sisters. The famous Cleopatra (Cleopatra VI) came to the throne at the age of 17 on the understanding that she would marry her brother, and when he was killed she was nominally married to her younger brother, Ptolemy XV. The custom has been fairly frequently found elsewhere and does not necessarily produce harmful physical results. Genesis 5. 4, of course, states clearly that Adam had sons and daughters: Hebrew tradition[1] says 33 sons and 23 daughters. The book of Jubilees (IV. 1. 9) says that Cain married his sister Awan. The 'city' is of course only the A.V. translation of a Hebrew term that could be used for a small settlement.

(6) Somewhat more difficult is Cain's fear of reprisal. He says, 'It shall come to pass that whosoever findeth me shall slay me', Genesis 4. 14 (R.V.). Josephus says Cain feared the beasts but the

---

[1] Quoted in footnote to Whiston's translation of *Josephus*, Antiq. Bk. 1. Ch. 11.

story seems clearly to imply that he feared human vengeance. It is easy to say that he feared vengeance from other sons of Adam, yet the story seems to imply that Seth was not born till after the murder had been committed. Nor does the story indicate that Abel had any children growing up—for if Cain did not marry till later what right have we to assume that Abel had already married one of his sisters? It is possible that under the awful mental stress of a murder recently done and at the same time with consciousness of the Presence of God Himself, Cain may have visualized the future with Adam's descendants multiplying down several generations, and the dread of vengeance, which seems to haunt so many, may have wrung the words from his lips. Some have argued that the story belongs to a much later time when the law of blood-vengeance for next-of-kin was a recognized law. Yet plainly this is not so, for God Himself protects Cain rather than causes his death, and the enactment of the law that 'whoso sheds man's blood by man must his blood be shed' is given much later. The whole evidence here is strange and no conclusive argument can be produced.

(7) The last line of possible Scriptural evidence for a race of co-Adamic beings, possibly derived from pre-Adamic, is drawn from Genesis 6. Here we are told that the 'sons of God' (sons of 'elohim) saw the 'daughters of men' from whom they chose wives. The offspring of this evidently unholy union are called 'nephilim' and they seem to be equated with the ancient heroes or 'men of renown'.

The term 'daughters of men' cannot be restricted to descendants of Seth. The term is 'daughters of Adam' i.e. human women. The term 'sons of elohim' is used twice more in the Bible, both times for angels, and this seems to rule out, though perhaps not finally, the possibility that the expression should be translated 'sons of the mighty ones' . . . i.e. surrounding warlike tribes or powerful leaders of some co-Adamic race. A strange possibility, however, does remain. If these 'sons of 'elohim' are indeed the fallen angels who, like Sodom and Gomorrah, fell into sexual crimes (see Jude 6 R.V.) bringing unholy nephilim (or the fallen-ones) into the world, we may ask in what shape or guise these beings could have intermarried with the human women. In the New Testament we find demons entering and controlling human bodies. Is it possible that the fallen angels of Genesis 6 seized the bodies of some co-Adamic beings and that these 'possessed' beings married 'daughters of Adam' . . . human women . . . having children who were great in stature and in evil? These are the beings the memory of whom lingers in the mythology of almost every ancient people and religion . . . the gods and the offspring of the gods, the giants and the titans. Such a corruption of the human race could only be dealt with by the destruction of those who had so degraded the race. Hence the Flood.

Once again the evidence cannot be lightly dismissed: once again it is inconclusive. If we may sum up the whole position it is evident that from the Old Testament account a case can be made out for the existence of co-Adamic and pre-Adamic 'man', but the case is far from conclusive, and perhaps not, on the whole, as strong as the evidence against it.

3. The third and final possible line of explanation is to see in Adam the first member of the human race; the ancestor of all who have ever lived who could be called human. This means that if Neandertal 'men' were indeed truly human they are descended from Adam, although their line showed signs of mutation and possibly degeneration and became extinct, while if it could be proved that they were not truly human, then by definition, they are not Adam's descendants. There are no insuperable difficulties here. All 'family trees' in books on evolution agree that Homo sapiens and Neandertal man had a common ancestor . . . that they are branches from some common stock. The view now before us would simply maintain that Homo sapiens has come of Sethite stock and it would admit that Adam had numerous other sons who may have given rise to other groups of early men.

The chief difficulty undoubtedly lies in chronology. Ussher puts Adam at 4004 B.C. The astronomical dating puts early man—if he was true man—at 500,000 B.C. It appears, at first, hopeless to bring these together. Yet it is possible that both scientists and the Bible are speaking of the same event and it is certainly unwise to abandon a study because of an initial difficulty.

I have already given—I trust humbly—my conviction that the astronomical datings for early man are not reasonable on scientific grounds. One is prepared to admit figures of the order of one or two thousands years for each stage in early man's modification of his tools . . . but this with all due stretching could surely not give

us dates beyond say 10,000 B.C. for Neolithic man[1] and 12,000
to 15,000 B.C. for the earliest Palaeolithic, and even these dates
seem to assume far too slow a development for men with the
intelligence shown by the cave drawings.

On the Biblical side it is well known that considerable problems
lie behind the attempt to date Noah's Flood, let alone the date of
Adam. True, the Hebrew text gives a list of genealogies with
ages, and on the simple interpretation of these it is quite easy to
get totals. But it must be confessed that the Hebrews in giving
genealogies often omitted names. To say that D was the son of A
was perfectly true in the Hebrew sense although, in fact, he
might have been the son of C who was the son of B who was the
son of A. Christ was the son of David, and Paul was a son of
Abraham in the Jewish sense. Matthew, in his first chapter,
speaks of the three sets of 14 generations between Abraham and
Christ though, in fact, he gives only 41 names, counting Jechoniah
twice, and omits three generations of kings. Further, where
Matthew gives 12 generations from Shealtiel to Christ Luke gives
20! In Ezra 7 the priest gives 17 generations between himself
and Aaron but if we use 1 Chronicles 6. 3-15 we get 23 generations,
with ample evidence that many are still missing, and if we compile
a more complete list from Ezra 7, 1 Chronicles 6 and the lists
given in *Josephus* and *Sedar Olam* we have the names of 41
generations (and there are still probably 3 or 4 missing) between
Aaron and Ezra.

If it be argued that the giving of the actual ages precludes the
possibility of a name being dropped out, the answer is that
matters are not as simple as this. In Genesis 11. 12 we read,
'And Arpachshad lived 35 years and begat Shelah . . . and Shelah
lived thirty years and begat Eber' . . . yet the LXX version reads,
'And Arphaxad lived 135 years and begat Cainan . . . and Cainan
lived 130 years and begat Sala . . . and Sala lived 130 years and
begat Heber'. We see, then, that it is not just a question of
accepting the Bible dates, but of finding the true Bible dates from
conflicting manuscript evidence both as to ages and the omission
of genealogies. It must be remembered, too, that when Luke gives

---

[1] In her final report on the excavations at Jericho Dr. Kenyon gives the
following radio-carbon dates:

     Earliest Pre-pottery neolithic (City A) . . . 6,800 B.C.
     Mesolithic settlements . . . . 7,890 B.C.

(*Pal. Exploration Quarterly*, 1960, pp. 98-100).
See also Note 1. p. 140.

the genealogy of our Lord he accepts the LXX reference to Cainan,[1] although it may be doubted whether it was in any of the Hebrew MSS. of his day.

The date of Abram at about 1900-2000 B.C., contemporary with the twelfth dynasty of Egypt, is established beyond any reasonable doubt. From then onwards the Hebrew dates are fairly fully given and, as Martin Anstey and others have shown, if allowance is made for the particular and sometimes curious ways in which the Jews reckoned periods of time, the whole yields a very good chronology. This is to be expected. The Jews were the children of Abraham. But all that goes before is a very brief summary of thousands of years. The present Hebrew MSS give, by addition, a mere 427 years from Abram back to the flood: the LXX makes it 1307 years! The recent discoveries among the manuscripts of the Dead Sea caves seem to suggest that sometimes the LXX accurately represents certain Hebrew MSS. which differed from the so-called Massoretic Text. Much has been said for and against the LXX chronology, yet one cannot help feeling that it gives the more reasonable span between Noah and Abram.

If Ussher's dates are admittedly too low owing to omission of generations and if the astronomical dates are admittedly too high and could be brought down to reasonable 'Archaeological' dates, the major difficulty—the chronological—disappears. Other much lesser problems remain and these are still days when dogmatism on such points is out of place. The data are insufficient for absolute certainty of interpretation and explanation, but one thing is certain, there is no irreconcilable difference between the essential teaching of the Bible on the one hand and the known facts of anthropology and archaeology on the other. Like some great jig-saw puzzle all the pieces do fit together. Maybe Bible students and scientists, having started from different edges, cannot yet quite see how their pieces will join up to make a complete picture . . . but the conclusion I have come to is that they do.

And if I may say it once more, this chapter has been an aside forced upon me by a desire to deal fairly with one of the great problems of our age. From this long aside we emerge once again into our main topic to bring the story of creation to its close in the great Sabbath rest of God.

---

[1] It is given in all Greek MSS. of Luke except Codex Bezae.

CHAPTER 19

THE SABBATH REST

And the heaven and the earth were finished,
And all the host of them.
And on the seventh day God finished His work which
He had made;
And He rested on the seventh day from all His work
which He had made.
And God blessed the seventh day,
And hallowed it:
because that in it
He rested from all His work
which God had created and made.

Gen. 2. 1-3 R.V.

WITH the creation of man and with his appointment as the vice-regent of God in the earth God's creative work was complete. Heaven and earth were finished. That which was finished was not, however, static. It was, and is, an ever-moving, changing, universe. God continues to control and uphold His universe. He rested from creating new things but not from maintaining His universe.

Man was the last new creature. Scientifically this is true, no new beings having appeared on this planet. Many minor changes have taken place; new varieties of plants and animals have appeared, some by natural crossing, some by human control, but no new order of beings has come into existence since man. New islands and mountains and lakes have come and some have gone: they are but part of a dynamic world: they are not things of a new order.

Only one completely new creation has been recorded—the Church, a spiritual reality of a different order from angelic hosts. God rested from creating new material things. The stage was set for His second great creation—a spiritual reality. Thus the rest of the Bible deals with that story . . . the testing of responsible beings . . . the sad story of their fall and the sad history of their self-centred, Creator-rejecting experience. Yet it moves on to the wonderful story of a great plan of redemption in Christ Jesus and of the calling and winning of the freely given homage and service and love of intelligent beings to a Saviour-Creator. As Adam in the beginning found a *bride* so Jesus Christ, Immanuel, finds as a *bride* those who will love Him and serve Him and whom He loves and for whom He died, and the plan is worked out to the astonishment of angels and for the instruction of endless ages beyond.

God rested. The words for 'seven' and for 'sabbath' and for 'rest' are all very old. In Hebrew they all start with the same two letters, S . . . B even though the B is often pronounced V. The root runs through many languages even to this day as we see in the English *seven*, the Latin *septem*, the German *sieben*. The Hebrew for rest is *shabath* and for seven is *sheba'*. To the Hebrews, rest and seven and sabbath were all connected.

It has sometimes been asserted that the Hebrews got the idea of the sabbath from the Babylonians. This is not so. The Babylonians in one or two of their months had 'lucky' days, namely the 7th, 14th, 19th, 21st, and 28th, on which the king was not supposed to perform certain acts. These days seem to be connected with some lunar scheme, and as the Babylonian months were not exactly 28 days it is plain that the lucky days do not follow a continuous seven-day sequence such as the Bible demands. It is also quite true that the word *sapattu* is applied by the Babylonians to the 15th day of the month, but this very fact shows that it was not part of a seven-day sequence. It is also true that one of these Babylonian days is called 'the day of rest to the heart', but even here the meaning seems to be rest to the heart of the god to whom some offering was to be made, and not rest to the human servant. *The Encyclopaedia Britannica* is doubtless right when it maintains that the Babylonian *shapattum* and the Hebrew *shabbath* are both derived from a far older word, now lost, from that primitive language which lies behind them both. The Hebrews kept the original meaning of the word in their words for seven and for rest. The Babylonians lost the original force of the expression, and hence it is clear that the Hebrews did not borrow from the Babylonian.

God rested on the seventh day. Why should He do this? The expression may be anthropomorphic, for the Eternal God needs no day's rest even from so great a task as creation. Surely it is but carrying on the figure which has run through the whole story. God is pictured reverently as a Great Workman. His rest proves beyond doubt that the task was finished. Indeed that is what the text stresses . . . God finished His work . . . it was complete . . . it was very good.

Yet surely there is more. God, if we may reverently say so, sets us an example, as He often does, which He desires us to follow, and to follow for our own good. The plan of one day's rest in seven is essentially good. Our bodies are designed to work at maximum efficiency if they are given one day's rest in seven from heavy manual tasks. Our minds grow weary unless once every seven days we can forget the routine of office, of factory or of profession. Our spirits grow weak if they are never given time to rise above the incessant round of the everyday and to rise at last above the narrow valleys of life to the contemplation of the things which are not seen but which are eternal. We need to look back in wonder at creation planned, revealed and completed, and to look forward in hope to that time when He, who for the joy that was before Him, having endured the Cross, shall see of the travail of His soul and be satisfied.

It has been truly said that we live in an age when meditation is a lost art. Surely it is one of the most priceless blessings given to man as an intelligent being. He can look back over every task he has finished, surveying it critically, and if it is well done he can rest, satisfied. God meant us to work, but He meant us to rest from work and to have time to survey all we have done—and also all that He has done. So, to show us the way, God Himself rested when the task was done; He surveyed His work; He pronounced it 'very good'. He rested in the joy of seeing that it was all perfectly prepared for what He had in view. And when that next long task is finished and the history of our race is brought to its conclusion, then there will still remain a far greater Sabbath, the Sabbath of God Himself, into which we are invited to enter.

Thus meditating we shall worship Him who, having planned and made a material universe that was very good, works on to complete His New Creation. Those who find time for such meditation find also that the great problems of life and death and pain and evil begin to slip down into a vast pattern, as yet only vaguely discerned but nevertheless certain. This pattern or answer is symbolised in the last book of the Bible in the stupendous vision of the once crucified, now glorified, Christ, in the centre of His universe, surrounded by the innumerable hosts of the redeemed and attended by the admiring wonder of other cosmic intelligences.

So meditating, the human soul begins to enter the great Sabbath Rest of God Himself.

BIBLIOGRAPHY

ABELSON, P. H.	*Researches in Geochemistry* New York, 1959.
ALFORD, Dean H.	*Commentary on Genesis* London, 1872.
ANSTEY, Rev. M.	*Romance of Bible Chronology* London, 1913.
BAILEY, Sir E. and WEIR, J.	*Introduction to Geology* London, 1939.
BARNES, Dr. H.	*Chemical aspects of Oceanography* R.I.C. Lectures and Reports No. 4 1955.
BATES, Prof. D. R.	*Space Research and Exploration* London, 1957.
„	*The Planet Earth* London, 1957.
BEASLEY, W. J.	*Creation's Amazing Architect* London, 1955.
BOTLEY, C. M.	*The Air and its Mysteries* London, 1938.
BOULENGER, E. G.	*A Natural History of the Seas* London, 1935.
BOWEN, E. J., F.R.S.	*The Chemical aspects of Light* Oxford, 1942.
BOWEN, Dr. R.N.	*The Exploration of Time* London, 1958.
BROWN, F., DRIVER, Prof. S. R. and BRIGGS, C. A.	*A Hebrew and English Lexicon of the Old Testament* Oxford, 1955.
BRUNNER, EMIL	*Christianity and Civilisation* London, 1948.
CARTER, G. S.	*Animal Evolution* London, 1951.
CARSON, RACHEL L.	*The Sea around us* London, 1951.
CHARLESWORTH, J. K.	*The Ice Age and the Future of Man.* Science Progress, 1953.
CLARK, Dr. R. E. D.	Darwin: *Before and After* London, 1948.
„	*The Universe: Plan or Accident* London, 1961.
„	*Christian Belief and Science* London, 1960.
COLMAN, J. S.	*The Sea and its Mysteries* London, 1950.
COULSON, Prof. C. A.	*Science and Christian Belief* Oxford, 1955.
CROMPTON, J.	*The Living Sea* London, 1957.
DAVIES, B.	*Hebrew and Chaldee Lexicon* London, 1876.
DEWAR, D.	*Is Evolution a myth?* London, 1949.
DAWSON, Sir J. W.	*Modern Science in Bible Lands* London, 1888.
DRIVER, Prof. G. R.	*Birds in the Old Testament* Palestine Exploration Quarterly, April and October, 1955.
GEIKIE-COBB, Dr. I.	*The Glands of Destiny* London, 1947.
GOSSE, P. H.	*Omphalos. An attempt to untie the geological knot* London, 1857.
HEIDEL, Prof. A.	*The Gilgamesh Epic and Old Testament Parallels* Chicago, 1949.
„	*The Babylonian Genesis* Chicago, 1951.
HELLMUTH, J.	*Biblical Thesaurus. Genesis* London, 1884.
HEUVELMANS, Dr. B.	*On the Track of Unknown Animals* London, 1959.

HOYLE, Prof. F.   *Frontiers of Astronomy* London, 1955.
HUXLEY, Sir J. S.   *Evolution, the Modern Synthesis* London, 1942.
JAMESON, W.   *The Wandering Albatross* London, 1958.
JENKINS, Dr. J. T.   *Whales and Modern Whaling* London, 1932.
JOLY, Prof. J.   *The Surface-History of the Earth* Oxford, 1925.
LACK, Prof. D.   *The Natural Regulation of Animal Numbers*
                         Oxford, 1954.
LANE, F. W.   *The Kingdom of the Octopus* London, 1957.
LIBBY, Prof. W. F.   *Radio-carbon dating*. Proc. Chem. Soc., May
                         1960.
      ,,   *Radiocarbon dating* Chicago, 1955.
LULL, R. S.   *Organic Evolution* New York, 1936.
MAUNDER, E. W.   *The Astronomy of the Bible* London, 1908.
MELDAU, Fred. J.   *Why we believe in Creation not in Evolution*
                         Denver, 1959.
MIXTER, Prof. R. L.   *Evolution and Christian Thought today* London,
                         1959.
MOORE, RUTH   *Man, Time and Fossils* London, 1954.
MORRIS, HENRY M. and   *The Genesis Flood* Philadelphia, 1962.
  WHITCOMB, J. C. Jr.
NORRISH, R. G. W.   *Some isothermal reactions of free radicals* (A
                         discussion of the earth's atmosphere). Proc.
                         Chem. Soc., Sept., 1958.
OAKLEY, K. P. and   *Reconsideration of the Galley Hill Skeleton*.
  MONTAGU, M. F.   Bulletin of the British Museum, Natural
                         History (Geology), Vol. 1. No. 2. 1949.
OAKLEY, K. P., WEINER, J. S. *The Solution of the Piltdown Problem* Ibid. Vol. 2.
  and LE GROS CLARK, W. E.   No. 3. London, 1953.
PAYNE, D. F.   *Genesis One Reconsidered* London, 1964.
PEMBER, G. H.   *Earth's earliest ages* London, 1891.
PENN, GRANVILLE   *Mineral and Mosaic Geologies* London, 1822.
PLACE, R.   *Finding Fossil Man* London, 1957.
RAMM, Dr. B.   *The Christian View of Science and Scripture*
                         London, 1955.
RIDDERBOS, Prof. N.   *Is there a conflict between Genesis 1 and Natural
                         Science?* Grand Rapids, Michigan, 1957.
ROGERS, R. W.   *Cuneiform Parallels to the Old Testament* New
                         York, 1926.
SENET, ANDRÉ   *Man in search of his ancestors* London, 1955.
SEWARD, Prof. A. C.   *Plant Life through the Ages* Cambridge, 1933.
SHORT, Prof. A. RENDLE   *Modern Discovery and the Bible* London, 1949.
SHUTE, Evan   *Flaws in the Theory of Evolution* London,
                         Canada, 1961.
SKINNER, Dr. J.   *Genesis. International Critical Commentary*
                         Edinburgh, 1930.
SMART, Prof. W. M.   *The Origin of the Earth* London, 1955.
STUART, Prof. A.   *Genesis and Geology* Evangelical Quarterly,
                         Vol. 1. No. 4, 1929.

SVERDRUP, JOHNSON and FLEMING   *The Oceans*   New York, 1942.

THOMSON, Prof. J. A.   *The Biology of Birds*   London, 1923.

VELIKOWSKY, I.   *Worlds in Collision*   London, 1950.

„   *Earth in Upheaval*   New York, 1955.

VESEY-FITZGERALD, B.   *Background to Birds*   London, 1948.

WENDT, H.   *I looked for Adam*   London, 1955.

WESTOLL, Prof. T. S.   *Studies on the Fossil Vertebrates*   London, 1958.

WISEMAN, P. J.   *New Discoveries in Babylonia about Genesis* London.

„   *Creation revealed in six days*   London, 1948.

WRIGHT, G. F.   *Scientific confirmations of Old Testament History* London, 1907.

WRIGHT, W. B.   *The Quaternary Ice Age*   London, 1937.

YOUNG, EDW. J.   *An Introduction to the Old Testament*   London, 1949.

ZEUNER, Prof. F. E.   *Dating the Past*   London, 1958.

INDEX